JOIN THE HORNBY CLUB

Join the Hornby Club from just £15 per year to access exclusive news and views from Hornby, plus a whole host of member benefits!

YOUR MEMBERSHIP INCLUDES:

- 10% discount* at Hornby.com for the duration of your membership
- Club welcome pack with membership card
- Access to exclusive Hornby models – only available to club members
- £20 voucher** to spend on exclusive Hornby models
- 3 Club magazines and 1 Winter Edition
- Priority pre-order access on selected lines
- Competitions including chances to win entry to events and brilliant prizes
- Discounted entry to various UK attractions
- Junior section with competitions and news

* Discount applies to full price items and cannot be used in conjunction with any other offer
** Cannot be used in conjunction with any other offer

COLLECTORS CLUB	VOUCHER	1 YEAR
Download	£20	£15.00
UK Postal	£20	£20.00
EU Postal	£20	£25.00

Join the Club and take advantage of our range of Hornby Club Exclusives that are only available to Club members. Remember, if you join you will receive a £20 voucher to spend on exclusive club models!

For more information about the Hornby Club please call our dedicated club helpline 01843 233512 or email us at newclubs@hornby.com

What's inside the magazine information:

- Exclusive behind-the-scenes Hornby news
- Event Information
- Special offers and competitions
- Latest product releases
- Historical Articles
- Members Gallery
- Junior section

3 CLUB MAGAZINES & 1 WINTER EDITION

10% DISCOUNT on Hornby brand products

SPECIAL OFFERS on magazines, books, admissions, Club kits

£20 VOUCHER to spend on club exclusive models – online and over the phone

JOIN US ONLINE
there is a community of Hornby fans waiting to connect!

www.hornby.com    /hornbyhobbiesltd   @hornby    /officialhornby

Contents

Like us!
facebook.com/officialhornby

Follow us!
twitter.com/hornby

Watch us!
youtube.com/hornbyhobbiesltd

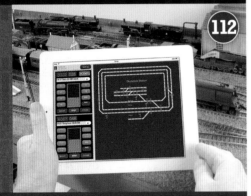
112

2016 RANGE PREVIEW!

FEATURES

FULL 2016 RANGE

64

14

CONTENTS

HORNBY® 2016 HANDBOOK

EDITOR: Mike Wild
ASSISTANT EDITOR: Mark Chivers
SUB EDITOR: Andrew Roden
DESIGNERS: Tracey Mumby and Steve Diggle
CONTRIBUTORS: Evan Green-Hughes, Ian Goodman, Paul Chetter, Martin Howard, Tim Shackleton, Ian Wild and Julia Scarlett.
HORNBY MARKETING: Montana Hoeren
PRODUCTION MANAGER: Janet Watkins

COMMERICAL DIRECTOR: Ann Saundry
MANAGING DIRECTOR: Adrian Cox
EXECUTIVE CHAIRMAN: Richard Cox

PUBLISHER: Key Publishing Ltd, PO Box 100, Stamford, Lincolnshire PE9 1XQ, United Kingdom.

DISTRIBUTION: Seymour Distribution Ltd, 2 Poultry Avenue, London EC1A 9PP Tel: 020 7429 4000

PRINTING: Precision Colour Printing Ltd, Haldane, Halesfield, Telford, Shropshire TF7 4QQ

HORNBY HOBBIES LIMITED:
3rd Floor, The Gateway, Innovation Way, Discovery Park, Sandwich CT13 9FF. United Kingdom
www.hornby.com
www.humbrol.com

Welcome

Hornby is synonymous with model railways and this year we are proud to produce the first Hornby Handbook - dedicated to bringing railway modellers of all ages and interests an exciting and insightful start to the hobby.

This time of year has traditionally been rich with anticipation in the build-up towards the annual catalogue launch. Within this Handbook is the full range of items which are coming to your local Hornby dealer in 2016. Whether your interest is steam or diesel there's sure to be something to whet your appetite for new modelling projects. 2015 has been different as significant elements from the 2016 plan have already been announced, but there is much more to come as the following pages reveal.

The coming year promises to be exciting for many reasons – not least because Hornby is producing five new locomotives, two new rakes of carriages and two new wagons alongside a list of re-releases from the existing portfolio. This stretches to more than 290 items!

It is these new additions which keep the hobby vibrant. In the past 12 months seven new locomotives have reached the shops ranging from the delightful Worsdell 'J15' and Drummond '700' 0-6-0s through to the mighty Collett 'King' express 4-6-0 and the elegant Holden 'D16/3' 4-4-0. 2015 will also be remembered for the launch of the RailRoad Crosti boilered '9F' 2-10-0

too as well as new ranges of carriages, wagons and the widespread introduction of Twin Track Sound for diesel locomotives.

You can relive the highlights of 2015 in a special feature looking back on the past year but the most exciting element of this Handbook is the future. Projects are what makes this hobby tick and this fresh Handbook is packed full of modelling tips and techniques put together by recognised modellers.

Inside you can learn how to lay track, make a basic baseboard, install a digital decoder, get the best from Hornby's Twin Track Sound locomotives and much more. Plus - if you're seeking inspiration for your layout there's a guide to building a tunnel and developing a station using the Hornby Skaledale collection as a detailed and authentic basis.

As always the Hornby Development Team is hard at work creating new models for everyone to enjoy. The 'Engine Shed Blog' on www.hornby.com is an ideal way of keeping up to date with the latest projects while Hornby's social media sites are a great way to stay in touch and showcase your projects too.

Enjoy the Handbook and, most importantly, enjoy modelling our wonderful railways!

Mike Wild
Hornby Handbook Editor

Steam reigns supreme with
4 *new* locomotives

Highlighting the diversity of steam locomotive design and the capabilities of the Hornby Development Team, the 2016 steam range sees the arrival of four new locomotives ranging in size from the impressive Bulleid air-smoothed 'Merchant Navy' right down to the diminutive Peckett 'W4' 0-4-0ST. Completing the line-up are brand new models of the Holden 'B12/3' 4-6-0 and Raven 'Q6' 0-8-0, both of which fill significant gaps in the range of ready-to-run steam motive power.

All four products are being designed from the ground up to meet the high expectations of modellers and will be available progressively through the year. The original condition 'Merchant Navy' is an important addition and a missing link in express passenger motive power in 'OO' gauge, while the 2015 released 'J15' 0-6-0 and 'D16/3' 4-4-0 will be suitably complemented with the arrival of the Great Eastern Region operated 'B12/3' 4-6-0 – a class which has a long history with Hornby through previous models.

The 'Q6,' meanwhile, marks a first foray into producing a North Eastern Region prototype – an area not covered in great detail by ready-to-run products – while the Peckett 'W4' 0-4-0ST is an industrial locomotive with great character which could be seen operating on private railways across the country.

Hornby's latest steam range is set to wow with four brand new locomotives joining its ranks in 2016. We reveal the full story on the new additions together with a detailed listing of new releases for the year ahead.

Steam reliveries

New tooling is just part of the story for the year ahead though as Hornby also has a list of more than 60 new locomotives to be released through the year using its extensive range of existing locomotives. This includes new versions of the 'J50' 0-6-0T, Adams '0415' 4-4-2T, 'D16/3' and 'S15' 4-6-0 from the 2015 new tooling lines and much more.

Following in the tradition of previous year's 'Great Gathering' and 'Silver Jubilee' collections, a special set of the locomotives is to be released to mark the 140th anniversary of Sir Nigel Gresley's birth and the 75th anniversary of his death. The collection features Gresley designed 'A1' 2554

Woodwinder, 'A3' 2503 *Firdaussi*, 'A4' 4494 *Osprey* and 'P2' 2001 *Cock O' the North* - the latter with a gloss finish - with each being produced as limited edition with a certificate of authenticity.

The range also sees the return of many favourites with new identities including the Drummond 'T9' 4-4-0 and Maunsell 'King Arthur' 4-6-0 for the Southern, the Churchward 'Star' and Collett 'Grange' 4-6-0s for the Western, the Stanier streamlined 'Princess Coronation' 4-6-2 and Fowler 2-6-4T for the Midland and the Thompson 'L1' 2-6-4T and 'O1' 2-8-0 for the Eastern.

For the full listing of 2016 locomotives see Table on page 12.

Air-smoothed Bulleid 'Merchant Navy' 21C19 *French Line CGT* storms through Vauxhall with the Down 'Bournemouth Belle' from London Waterloo-Bournemouth in 1947. Railphotoprints.co.uk.

❶ The 'Merchant Navy'

Hornby has a great history with the Bulleid 4-6-2 designs as it was the rebuilt 'Merchant Navy' which relaunched the company in 2000. The original air-smoothed 'Merchant Navy' design has long been requested and it will now be joining the range in 2016. Hornby has led the charge in contemporary models of Southern Railway/ Region prototypes with the Maunsell 'S15' and 'N15' 4-6-0s, Drummond 'T9' 4-4-0, '700' 0-6-0 and 'M7' 0-4-4T, Bulleid 'Q1' 0-6-0, air-smoothed and rebuilt 'West Country'/'Battle of Britain' 4-6-2s together with the aforementioned rebuilt 'Merchant Navy' all forming part of its catalogue.

The new air-smoothed 'Merchant Navy' will allow for all three major variants to be produced, but in its first year Hornby will be releasing locomotives based on the first and third series of the 30-strong class. The model will feature a fully detailed air-smoothed body shell matching the detail differences between the different build series, a new air-smoothed tender for the original series and an all new 6,000gallon tender for the third series locomotives. The comprehensively designed tooling means that all 30 locomotives can be modelled

in the future and Hornby acknowledges the support of the Bulleid Society, Graham Muspratt and Mike King in development of this new model.

On release Hornby the 'Merchant Navy' will be released in Southern Railway lined malachite green livery with 'sunshine' Southern lettering on the tender and original Bulleid numbers as 21C1 *Channel Packet* and 21C3 *Royal Mail* - both featuring detail differences together with BR lined green livery with early crests as 35028 *Clan Line*. A Twin Track Sound version will also be released as 35023 Holland Afrika Line in BR lined green.

The model will feature an 8-pin Digital Command Control (DCC) decoder socket in the tender. Provision will also be made for the addition of DCC sound with a housing for a 28mm round speaker being built into the tender chassis. Other features include a fully detailed cab interior, NEM coupling pockets front and rear with small tension lock couplings and a comprehensive detailing pack including bufferbeam fittings and brake rigging.

For the history of the 'Merchant Navy' 4-6-2 see pages 16-21.

'MERCHANT NAVY' MODEL SPECIFICATION

Bulleid 'Merchant Navy' details	
Cat No:	R3434
Livery:	21C1 *Channel Packet*, SR malachite green
Cat No:	R3435
Livery:	21C3 *Royal Mail*, SR malachite green
Cat No:	R3436
Livery:	35028 *Clan Line*, BR lined green, early crests
Couplings:	Small tension locks in NEM pockets
DCC:	DCC ready, 8-pin socket
Scale:	'OO'
Features:	Tender mounted decoder socket, provision for speaker, first and third series locomotives.

The new 'B12' will have a fully detailed cab together with different air-pump styles to suit different locomotives.

② The 'B12/3' 4-6-0

The Holden 'B12' 4-6-0 has a long history with Hornby. Its first ready-to-run model of the inside cylinder passenger locomotive arrived in 1962 and, after many updates and modifications, the last versions were produced in 2011 for use in trainsets.

However, 2016 will see the release of a brand new 'B12' produced to the high standards that Hornby's steam locomotive range demands - making this highly sought after Great Eastern Region locomotive fit to stand alongside the 'J15' 0-6-0 and 'D16' 4-4-0 released in 2015.

Hornby's new model will focus on the 'B12/3' variant – a sub-class introduced in 1932 with the fitting of new larger diameter boilers. The

last of these remained in traffic until 1961 - 61572 - which was later preserved at the North Norfolk Railway where it is fully restored to working order. The Great Eastern Railway Society and the North Norfolk Railway have both assisted in production of the new model.

The new tooling for the 'B12/3' will feature a highly detailed body, different Westinghouse air pump designs, smooth and riveted smokeboxes and the choice of fluted and plain coupling rods. It will also have an 8-pin DCC decoder socket in the tender together with space for a 28mm round speaker designed in for DCC sound users. The tender will be permanently coupled to the locomotive with a

metal drawbar.

Three versions are planned for release in the first year of the new 'B12' covering London and North Eastern Railway (LNER) apple

green (R3430), BR lined black with early crests (R3431) and BR lined black with late crests (R3432).

For the history of the 'B12' 4-6-0 see pages 100-105.

'B12/3' MODEL SPECIFICATION

Holden 'B12/3' details	
Cat No:	R3430
Livery:	LNER apple green
Cat No:	R3431
Livery:	BR lined black, early crests
Cat No:	R3432
Livery:	BR lined black, late crests
Couplings:	Small tension locks in NEM pockets
DCC:	DCC ready, 8-pin socket
Scale:	'OO'
Features:	Tender mounted decoder socket, provision for speaker, smooth and riveted smokebox types, fluted and plain coupling rods

Holden 'B12/3' 4-6-0 61541 heads away from Sincil Junction, Lincoln, with a train for Grantham on August 28 1954. These fine 4-6-0s are being recreated with a brand new model for 2016. Bob Tuck/Rail Archive Stephenson.

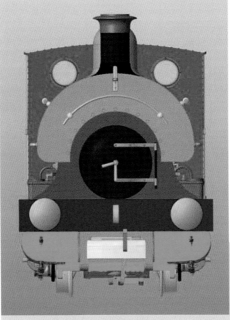

'W4' MODEL SPECIFICATION

Peckett 'W4' details	
Cat No:	R3427
Livery:	563, industrial green
Cat No:	R3428
Livery:	654, dark green and red
Cat No:	R3429
Livery:	832, dark blue and red
Couplings:	Small tension locks in NEM pockets
DCC:	DCC ready, 4-pin socket
Scale:	'OO'
Features:	Fully detailed cab interior, compact 4-pin decoder socket

The Peckett 'W4' 0-4-0ST is one of the smallest steam locomotives to be produced for 'OO'. It launched in October on the Hornby Engine Shed Blog.

❸ The Peckett 'W4' 0-4-0ST

New to the line up for 2016 is Hornby's first all new industrial steam locomotive since introduction of the Hunslet 'Austerity' 0-6-0ST in 1998 – the diminutive Peckett 'W4' 0-4-0ST.

Introduced in 1885 the 'W4' was used across a variety of industries including collieries and steelworks. Its small wheelbase made it ideal for shunting purposes and the design received many revisions once in traffic through respective owners. Examples of the 'W4' were operated by the National Coal Board as well as the London Midland & Scottish Railway (LMS) and Great Western Railway (GWR).

Hornby's new model of the 'W4' 0-4-0ST follows in the footsteps of the Sentinel 4wDH shunter introduced in 2014 in having a small four-wheel chassis. The Peckett will be DCC ready using a 4-pin socket arrangement and the tooling will feature both plastic and die-cast construction to ensure the model has adequate weight for haulage.

Details of the liveries were in the early stages of planning in late 2015 with the model expected to be released towards the end of summer 2016.

For the history of the Peckett 'W4' 0-4-0ST see pages 120-123.

Class	Description	Period	Cat. No.
GWR 'Star' 4-6-0	4013 *Knight of St Patrick*, GWR lined green	1930s/1940s	R3455
GWR '42XX' 2-8-0T	4287, BR black, late crests	1950s/1960s	R3462
GWR 'Castle' 4-6-0	5076 *Drysllwyn Castle*, GWR shirt button lined green	1930s	R3454
GWR '5205' 2-8-0T	5231, BR black, early crests	1950s	R3463
GWR 'King' 4-6-0	6016 *King Edward V*, GWR shirtbutton green	1930s	R3408
GWR 'King' 4-6-0	6002 *King William IV*, BR lined green, late crests	1960s	R3409
GWR 'King' 4-6-0	6025 *King Henry III*, BR lined blue, early crests	1950s	R3410
GWR 'Grange' 4-6-0	6825 *Llanfair Grange*, BR lined green, late crests	1950s/1960s	R3452
GWR '72XX' 2-8-2T	7224, BR black, late crests	1950s/1960s	R3464
SR 'Terrier' 0-6-0T	751, SECR lined green	1920s	R3467
SR 'T9' 4-4-0	116, Southern Railway olive green	1930s	R3457
SR '0415' 4-4-2T	3125, SR black with Bulleid lettering	1940s	R3422
SR '0415' 4-4-2T	30583, BR lined black, late crests	1950s/1960s	R3423
SR '700' 0-6-0	693, Southern Railway unlined black	1930s/1940s	R3419
SR '700' 0-6-0	30346, BR black, late crests	1950s/1960s	R3420
SR '700' 0-6-0	30698, BR black, early crests	1950s	R3421
SR 'King Arthur' 4-6-0	30792 *Sir Hervis de Revel*, BR lined green, early crests	1950s	R3456
SR 'S15' 4-6-0	827, Southern Railway black	1940s	R3411
SR 'S15' 4-6-0	30842, BR black, early crests	1950s	R3412
SR 'S15' 4-6-0	30831, BR black, late crests	1950s/1960s	R3413
SR 'Schools' 4-4-0	921 *Shrewsbury*, SR black with Bulleid lettering	1940s	R3458
SR 'West Country' 4-6-2 (air-smoothed)	34032 *Camelford*, BR lined green, early crests	1950s	R3445
SR 'Battle of Britain' 4-6-2 (rebuilt)	34077 *603 Squadron*, BR lined green, late crests	1950s/1960s	R3468
SR 'Merchant Navy' 4-6-2 (air-smoothed)	**21C1 *Channel Packet*, SR malachite green**	**1940s**	**R3434**
SR 'Merchant Navy' 4-6-2 (air-smoothed)	**21C3 *Royal Mail*, SR malachite green**	**1940s**	**R3435**
SR 'Merchant Navy' 4-6-2 (air-smoothed)	**35028 *Clan Line*, BR lined green**	**1950s**	**R3436**
LMS 'Princess Coronation' 4-6-2	6237 *City of Bristol*, LMS lined maroon (streamlined)	1930s	R3442
LMS Fowler 2-6-4T	42334, BR lined black, late crests	1950s/1960s	R3404
LMS 'Black Five' 4-6-0	45274, BR lined black, late crests	1950s/1960s	R3453
LNER 'A3' 4-6-2	60103 *Flying Scotsman*, BR lined green, late crests	1950s/1960s	R3443
LNER 'A4' 4-6-2	4499 *Sir Murrough Wilson*, NE wartime black	1940s	R3441
LNER 'B1' 4-6-0	61032 *Stembok*, BR lined black, early crests	1950s	R3451
LNER 'B12' 4-6-0	**LNER lined black**	**1930s/1940s**	**R3430**
LNER 'B12' 4-6-0	**BR lined black, early crests**	**1950s**	**R3431**
LNER 'B12' 4-6-0	**BR lined black, late crests**	**1950s/1960s**	**R3432**
LNER 'B17' 4-6-0	2842 *Kilverston Hall*, LNER lined apple green	1930s/1940s	R3447
LNER 'B17' 4-6-0	61619 *Welbeck Abbey*, BR lined green, early crests	1950s	R3448
LNER 'D16/3' 4-4-0	8900, LNER lined apple green	1930s/1940s	R3433
LNER 'J15' 0-6-0	5444, LNER black	1930s/1940s	R3414
LNER 'J15' 0-6-0	65477, BR black, early crests	1950s	R3415
LNER 'J15' 0-6-0	65464, BR black, late crests	1950s/1960s	R3416
LNER 'J50' 0-6-0T	586, LNER unlined black	1930s/1940s	R3405
LNER 'J50' 0-6-0T	Departmental No. 14, BR black, late crests	1950s/1960s	R3406
LNER 'J50' 0-6-0T	68959, BR black, early crests	1950s	R3407
LNER 'K1' 2-6-0	62065, BR lined black, late crests	1950s/1960s	R3417
LNER 'K1' 2-6-0	62006, British Railways black	1950s	R3418
LNER 'L1' 2-6-4T	67702, British Railways lined apple green	1950s	R3461
LNER 'N2' 0-6-2T	4765, LNER lined black	1930s/1940s	R3465
LNER 'O1' 2-8-0	6359, LNER black	1930s/1940s	R3446
LNER 'Q6' 0-8-0	**3418, LNER black**	**1930/1940s**	**R3424**
LNER 'Q6' 0-8-0	**63443, BR black, early crests**	**1950s**	**R3425**
LNER 'Q6' 0-8-0	**63429, BR black, late crests**	**1950s/1960s**	**R3426**
BR 'Britannia' 4-6-2	70034 *Thomas Hardy*, BR lined green, early crests	1950s	R3444
Hunslet 'Austerity' 0-6-0ST	22, United Steel Company maroon	1950s	R3466
Peckett 'W4' 0-4-0ST	**563, industrial green**	**1950s**	**R3427**
Peckett 'W4' 0-4-0ST	**654, dark green and red**	**1950s**	**R3428**
Peckett 'W4' 0-4-0ST	**832, dark blue and red**	**1920s**	**R3429**
LNER 'A1' 4-6-2	2554 *Woolwinder*, LNER lined apple green	1930s	R3439
LNER 'A3' 4-6-2	2503 *Firdaussi*, LNER lined apple green	1930s/1940s	R3437
LNER 'A4' 4-6-2	4494 *Osprey*, LNER lined apple green	1930s	R3438
LNER 'P2' 2-8-2	2001 *Cock 'O the North*, LNER lined apple green	1930s	R3440

NOTE: Models listed in bold are new toolings for 2016.

The much requested 'Q6' is at an advanced stage of development. This is the latest decorated sample of 0-8-0.

❹ The 'Q6' 0-8-0

Freight movement was an essential business for the steam era railway and nowhere more so than in the industrial North East. Here coal and iron ore had to be transported in heavily laden trains which called for something special. The 'Q6' 0-8-0 was introduced by Raven in 1913 for the sole purpose of moving heavy freight traffic with a total of 120 being built by 1921.

Traditionally - due to its small area and the limited sphere of operation for its locomotives - the North Eastern Region hasn't been a target for a ready-to-run model, but Hornby is changing all that in 2016 with a brand new

model of the much requested 'Q6'. Developed with assistance from the North Eastern Locomotive Preservation Group (which owns the only surviving 'Q6' 63395) and the North Yorkshire Moors Railway (the home of 63395) the new 'OO' scale 0-8-0 is set to impress.

The design brief calls for models of locomotives with smooth and riveted smokeboxes and different bufferbeams while focusing on the fleet in its post-1930 condition. It will also feature a powerful five pole motor in the locomotive coupled to a tender which will host an 8-pin DCC decoder socket and space for a 28mm round speaker for those

wishing to add digital sound to the completed model.

On release the 'Q6' will be available in LNER black (R3424), BR black with early crests (R3425) and BR black with late crests

(R3426). Running numbers had not been assigned in late 2015, but will be on *www.hornby.com* in the near future.

For the history of the 'Q6' 0-8-0 see pages 84-89. Ⓗ

'Q6' MODEL SPECIFICATION

Cat No:	R3424
Livery:	3418, LNER black
Cat No:	R3425
Livery:	63443, BR black, early crests
Cat No:	R3426
Livery:	63429, BR black, late crests
Couplings:	Small tension locks in NEM pockets
DCC:	DCC ready, 8-pin socket
Scale:	'OO'
Features:	Tender mounted decoder socket, provision for speaker

The North Eastern Railway 'Q6' 0-8-0 is to be reproduced in 'OO' by Hornby in 2016. In 1958 'Q6' 63348 passes Chaloners Whin with an Up goods.
Cecil Ord/Rail Archive Stephenson.

Class 71 electric leads the way in 2016

Hornby's reputation for quality diesel and electric models is well known. New for 2016 is the Southern Region Class 71 Bo-Bo electric, but that isn't all that is in store.

Building on its range of high profile diesel and electric locomotives the Hornby Development Team is generating a brand new ready-to-run model of the BR Class 71 Bo-Bo electric locomotive for release in 2016.

The Class 71 was announced at the 2014 Warley National Model Railway Exhibition at the National Exhibition Centre in Birmingham and immediately hit the headlines in the model press. The Class 71 was a unique design from the British Railways 1955 Modernisation Plan in that it was built to operate primarily from the Southern Region's 750v DC third-rail electrification system but was also fitted with a pantograph on the roof to allow current collection from overhead lines in goods yards where ground based electrical power was deemed too dangerous for staff.

The first Class 71s entered traffic in 1958 following construction at BR's Doncaster Works. In total 24 were delivered and in service by the end of 1960. Their time in front line service was short due to a reduction in suitable work for them, but they were well known for service on the prestigious 'Golden Arrow' Pullman train from London Victoria to Dover amongst other workings. For more on the history of the Class 71 see pages 48-53.

Hornby's model of the Class 71 has been tooled from scratch. Due to a lack of available drawings careful measuring of the sole surviving example – E5001 owned by the National Railway Museum – was carried out with full permission at the locomotive's current Barrow Hill Roundhouse base. A 3D laser scan was also taken of the Class 71 in order to check measurements and vital curve profiles of the complex cab design.

For the model's first year three versions are on the way covering

CLASS 71 MODEL SPECIFICATION

Number:	E5001
Livery:	As preserved BR green with small yellow warning panels and bodyside lining
Cat No:	R3373
Number:	71012
Livery:	BR blue with full yellow ends
Cat No:	R3374
Number:	E5022
Livery:	BR plain green with bodyside lining
Cat No:	R3376
Price:	£149.99
Couplings:	Small tension locks in NEM pockets
DCC:	DCC ready, 8-pin socket
Scale:	'OO'
Features:	Working pantograph, directional lighting, manual switch to control taillights

The Southern Region's Class 71 Bo-Bo electric is leading the Hornby diesel and electric range in 2016. On September 21 1966 E5021 passes through Ashford with a goods working. Colour Rail.

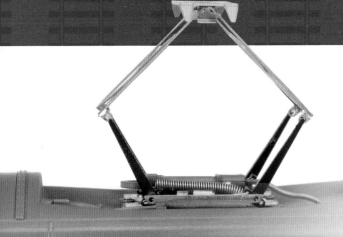

The new Hornby Class 71 is progressing rapidly. This is the second engineering prototype.

E5001 in as preserved BR green livery with small yellow warning panels (Cat No. R3373), 71012 in BR blue with full yellow ends (R3374) and E5022 in plain BR green, as delivered (R3376).

The model features a highly detailed body together with a comprehensively finished underframe which includes correct pattern spoked wheels and fully detailed bufferbeams with sprung buffers. The battery boxes in the centre of the underframe contain two switches – one to turn the tail lights off for when the locomotive is coupled to a train and second to allow current collection via the detailed pantograph which sits centrally on top of the locomotive. Added to this the Class 71 will feature an 8-pin DCC decoder socket, provision for the addition of a 15mm x 11mm speaker for DCC sound users, interior detail behind the large glazed side window, changeable route codes, directional lighting and a powerful five-pole motor with twin flywheel drive for optimum performance.

While the Class 71 is the only newly tooled locomotive in Hornby's 2016 diesel and electric range, a host of reliveries have been planned for release over the course of the year. Highlights include a new version of the Class 31 in BR green, a Class 50 in original style Network SouthEast colours, two new Class 56s, a pair of Class 153s and a Manchester Ship Canal liveried Sentinel 4wDH shunter

See Table, right, for the full list of planned new diesel and electric locomotives for 2016. Ⓗ

Both sides of the Class 71 feature correct detailing – and the pantograph can be used to collect power too!

2016 DIESEL AND ELECTRIC LOCOMOTIVES

Class	Description	Period	Cat No.
Class 08	13363, BR green, red con rods	1950s	R3484
Class 08	08644 *Laira Diesel Depot*, BR blue	2000s	R3485
Class 31	D5509, BR green	1960s	R3470
Class 43	43070 *The Corps of Royal Electric and Mechanical Engineers* and 43036, First Great Western	2000s	R3478
Class 50	50026 *Indomitable*, original Network SouthEast	1980s	R3471
Class 56	56018, EWS maroon and gold	1990s/2000s	R3472
Class 56	56108, BR Railfreight grey with red stripe	1980s	R3473
Class 66	66185 *DP World London Gateway*, DB Schenker red	2000s	R3486
Class 66	66079, EWS maroon and gold	2000s	R3487
Class 67	67025 *Western Star*, EWS maroon and gold	2000s	R3481
Class 71	**E5001, BR green with small yellow panels (NRM)**	**1990s/2000s**	**R3373**
Class 71	**71012, BR blue**	**1970s**	**R3374**
Class 71	**E5022, BR green**	**1950s/1960s**	**R3376**
Class 60	60066, Drax silver	2000s	R3479
Class 90	90015 *The International Brigades*, Virgin Trains	2000s	R3474
Class 90	90014 *Norfolk and Norwich Festival*, Greater Anglia	1990s	R3475
Class 92	92016 *Brahms*, Railfreight grey with EWS logos	2000s	R3480
Class 153	153327, Arriva Train Wales	2000s	R3476
Class 153	153321, Regional Railways	1990s	R3477
2-HAL	2623 BR blue with full yellow ends	1970s	R3341A
Sentinel 4wDH	DH16, Manchester Ship Canal blue	1960s	R3482
Sentinel 0-4-0	Crossley Evans pale blue	1960s	R3483

NOTE: Items marked in bold text are new tooling models for 2016

Bulleid's magnificent
'Merchant Navy'

Oliver Bulleid's ground breaking Southern Railway 'Pacifics' were amongst the most technologically advanced for their time. The larger 'Merchant Navy' type are perhaps the most famous, despite their flaws. With Hornby producing a new model of the air-smoothed original 'Merchant Navy' class Evan Green-Hughes looks at the history of this fascinating design.

By the 1930s the Southern Railway (SR) was largely electrified using the third-rail principle, but the company still had a need for steam engines for goods and for long distance passenger work. More specifically the lines to the West of England and to the South Coast around Southampton and beyond required locomotive haulage for heavy trains. At the time the Southern relied on 'Schools' 4-4-0s and 'Lord Nelson' 4-6-0s but these locomotives were not able to provide the sort of power to pull the longer, faster and heavier trains that the operating department wanted to run.

In autumn 1937 the company recruited Oliver Bulleid to the post of Chief Mechanical Engineer following the retirement of Richard Maunsell. Bulleid was not a young man at 55 years old but he was an innovator and he came from the London and North Eastern Railway, a company with a formidable reputation for providing powerful and fast engines. Bulleid was a breath of fresh air to the Southern and he at once set about improving the performance of the locomotives he found there by promoting upgrades to the exhausts and cylinders of existing engines as well as obtaining better coal and listening to the suggestions of his enginemen. However what was really needed was a new and more powerful fleet of locomotives that would be masters of any work offered to them.

A radical rethink

In considering what to do Bulleid was greatly influenced by the work he'd undertaken on the LNER's 'P2' 2-8-2s which had been designed to haul heavy expresses over the winding route between Edinburgh and Aberdeen. If he'd had his way the Southern would have had engines of this wheel arrangement but the civil engineering department vetoed them on the grounds of

Bulleid's 'Merchant Navy' 35011 *General Steam Navigation* departs Bournemouth Central with steam to spare heading an Up express for London Waterloo on May 4 1957. Gordon Hepburn/Rail Archive Stephenson.

Below: In original condition, but now with its British Railways number and tender lettering 'Merchant Navy' 4-6-2 35005 *Canadian Pacific* passes Winchfield with the Down 'Atlantic Coast Express' on September 2 1949. At the time 35005 was fitted experimentally with a Berkley mechanical stoker that Bulleid had acquired second-hand from Canada. E.C. Griffith/Rail Archive Stephenson.

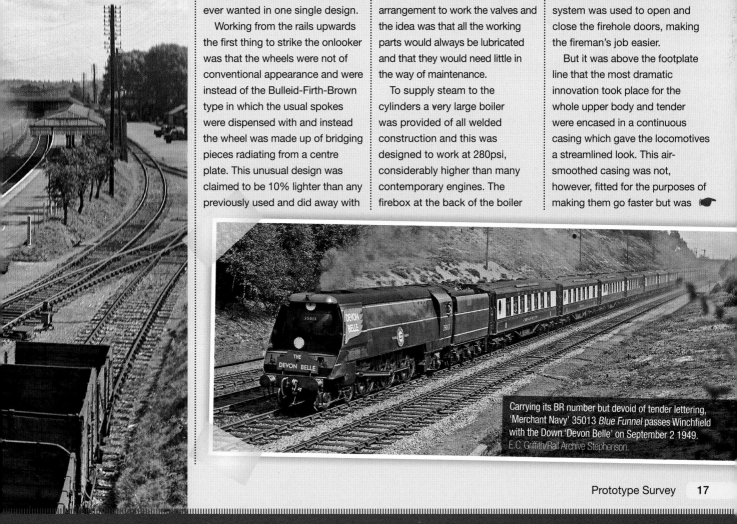

the long fixed wheelbase and so instead thoughts turned to the design of a fast, economical and modern 4-6-2.

What emerged from Eastleigh Works in 1941 was radically different from anything operating on any other railway. Having finally been given overall charge of designing a completely new engine so late in life, it was almost as though Bulleid wanted to incorporate every feature he had ever wanted in one single design.

Working from the rails upwards the first thing to strike the onlooker was that the wheels were not of conventional appearance and were instead of the Bulleid-Firth-Brown type in which the usual spokes were dispensed with and instead the wheel was made up of bridging pieces radiating from a centre plate. This unusual design was claimed to be 10% lighter than any previously used and did away with

the need for balancing weights.

Power was brought to these wheels from three cylinders, two outside the frames and one inside, which was a fairly normal arrangement, but what was really unusual was that the three sets of motion, the valve gear and other essential working parts were encased in an oil bath containing 40 gallons of lubricant and which was accommodated between the frames. Within this was a chain arrangement to work the valves and the idea was that all the working parts would always be lubricated and that they would need little in the way of maintenance.

To supply steam to the cylinders a very large boiler was provided of all welded construction and this was designed to work at 280psi, considerably higher than many contemporary engines. The firebox at the back of the boiler

was very wide too and was designed to be able to provide enough heat even when being fired with indifferent coal.

The engine was provided with a host of other innovations, not least electric lighting for indicator lamps and for crew use on the footplate and this was provided by power from a steam driven generator set. Ultra-violet light was used to illuminate the gauges in the cab and a steam operated system was used to open and close the firehole doors, making the fireman's job easier.

But it was above the footplate line that the most dramatic innovation took place for the whole upper body and tender were encased in a continuous casing which gave the locomotives a streamlined look. This air-smoothed casing was not, however, fitted for the purposes of making them go faster but was ☞

Carrying its BR number but devoid of tender lettering, 'Merchant Navy' 35013 *Blue Funnel* passes Winchfield with the Down 'Devon Belle' on September 2 1949. E.C. Griffith/Rail Archive Stephenson.

initially designed as an aid to lifting smoke away from the huge boiler and also so that the locomotive could be cleaned in a conventional carriage washing plant.

As if to emphasise all these departures from normal practice when it came to numbering what was to become the 'Merchant Navy' class Bulleid adopted a continental practice with which he had become familiar when working in Europe for Westinghouse. In this a series of letters and numbers are used to describe the wheel arrangement of the locomotive. The first locomotive 21C1, was so numbered because the 2 and the 1 refer to the number of unpowered leading and trailing axles and the C tells us that the number of driving axles is three, the final 1 is the actual number of the engine. 21C1 carried the name *Channel Packet* following a suggestion that the new class should be named after shipping lines that called at Southampton. It was followed shortly afterwards by 21C2 which was named *Union Castle*.

There then followed a long period of running in during which a number of issues with the design became apparent. Due to wartime restrictions the 'Merchant Navy' class had been designated as mixed traffic locomotives (their 6ft 2in diameter driving wheels just about scraping them through into this category) – though it still seems astonishing that Bulleid

got away with this given that they were clearly designed for fast passenger work.

Into traffic

Both engines were set to work on freight trains between Eastleigh and Salisbury and later they moved over to the Salisbury-Exeter route. Both were found to be considerably over their estimated weight and so steps had to be taken to lighten them. Holes were subsequently bored in the mainframes of the first two and in the following three

engines after which the frames were redesigned and seven of the class initially had external sheeting made up of limpet board instead of metal. A chimney cover designed for use in the carriage washer was also removed.

Exhaust steam drifting around the front end was a problem despite the casing, and so short smoke deflectors were fitted to the first ten engines and became a standard fitting on construction after that. There was also something of a minor redesign from 21C10 onwards with the

height of the engine being reduced slightly and different valves being fitted. The cab and the tender were also altered so that the cab side sheets turned inwards at the rear and were glazed on the upper portion of this return. The tender had a new space provided for fire irons too.

By 1942 the class had begun work on passenger trains between London and Exeter with some success. Loads of up to 20 coaches were reported on some services but smoke around the front end remained a problem with the result that longer smoke deflectors were fitted. Locomotives from the 21st onwards did not carry their continental style number as they were delivered after nationalisation – instead they received the new British Railways five digit number series starting 35021. Ultimately the class was numbered 35001-35030.

Eye catching liveries adorned the air-smoothed 'Merchant Navy' class too with their first colour scheme being malachite green lined in yellow and sporting Southern lettering on the tender. On nationalisation in 1948 the Southern lettering was replaced with British Railways as a stop gap while the newly formed state railway designed its own corporate identity. This was followed, for a few locomotives, by repainting in BR express lined blue – a short lived experimental colour scheme – but ultimately all received standard BR lined green livery with early cycling lion crests.

From 1948 onwards an amended cab design was introduced which had a pronounced wedge shape to the front, making the cab bigger and also providing larger windows for the crew to view signals. This modification was eventually applied to the whole class over the following years. By this time the class was almost wholly employed on express work where they gained a reputation for being free steaming and fast-running engines, a reputation that also extended to their lighter and smaller cousins the 'Battle of Britain' and 'West Country' classes. ☛

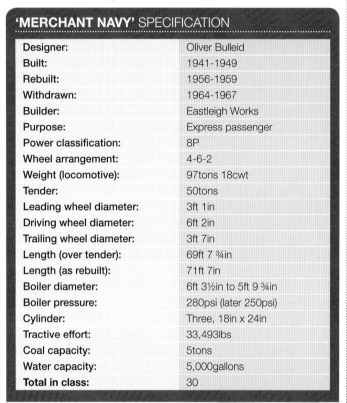

'MERCHANT NAVY' SPECIFICATION

Designer:	Oliver Bulleid
Built:	1941-1949
Rebuilt:	1956-1959
Withdrawn:	1964-1967
Builder:	Eastleigh Works
Purpose:	Express passenger
Power classification:	8P
Wheel arrangement:	4-6-2
Weight (locomotive):	97tons 18cwt
Tender:	50tons
Leading wheel diameter:	3ft 1in
Driving wheel diameter:	6ft 2in
Trailing wheel diameter:	3ft 7in
Length (over tender):	69ft 7 ¾in
Length (as rebuilt):	71ft 7in
Boiler diameter:	6ft 3½in to 5ft 9 ¾in
Boiler pressure:	280psi (later 250psi)
Cylinder:	Three, 18in x 24in
Tractive effort:	33,493lbs
Coal capacity:	5tons
Water capacity:	5,000gallons
Total in class:	30

35022 *Holland America Line* – the second of the BR built 'Merchant Navys' – undergoes testing on the rollers inside Rugby Testing Station on April 8 1953. Jim Jarvis/On-Line Transport Archive/Rail Archive Stephenson.

In fine style 'Merchant Navy' 35027 *Port Line* – now preserved in rebuilt form - passes Folkestone Junction with a Dover Marine-London Victoria boat train on June 7 1954. *Gordon Hepburn/Rail Archive Stephenson.*

After rebuilding the 'Merchant Navy' class took on a much more conventional form, not dissimilar to the BR Standard 'Britannia' class 'Pacific' – although clearly still of Bulleid origin with their oval smokebox door and Bulleid-Firth-Brown wheels. On July 15 1964 35012 *United States Line* approaches Vauxhall soon after leaving London Waterloo with the 6.30pm to Bournemouth. BR 4-EPB 5332 runs parallel with empty coaching stock. *Brian Stephenson.*

Bulleid's new 'Pacific' design was in sharp contrast to other locomotives of the early 1940s. The first of the class 21C1 *Channel Packet* poses for its official photograph when new in 1941. *RAS Collection.*

Teething troubles

Unfortunately as might have been expected from such an innovative design, there were problems, particularly with the oil bath arrangement which was prone to leaks and caused a number of fires on locomotives and track. The steam reverser also proved to be difficult for drivers to operate accurately and there were continuing problems with smoke drifting back over the boiler. Maintenance costs were also more than expected and finance had to be found for modifications necessary after the engines were built.

After the nationalisation of the railway system in January 1948 Oliver Bulleid left for a new position in Ireland and following his departure there was an unwillingness amongst senior British Railways managers to persist with some of the more advanced features of the 'Merchant Navy'. Cab modifications continued and a programme of cutting down the streamlined sides of the tenders began so that it was easier for the water column bags to be swung over the sides but otherwise attempts to improve the existing design ceased.

In March 1954 35020 *Bibby Line* became the first 'Merchant Navy' to have its boiler pressure reduced from 280psi to 250psi bringing it more into line with contemporary practice but running costs were still high and consequently in November 1955 35018 *British India Line* went into Eastleigh works for a radical rework, emerging the following February. This rebuilt engine was shorn of its troublesome oil bath and associated equipment and instead was fitted with standard Walschaert's valve gear – the most common in British locomotive design.

Its steam reverser had been removed too and replaced with the screw type and a new inside cylinder had been fitted. To the observer the most noticeable change was that the air-smoothed casing had been removed, revealing the

boiler and that a high running plate had been fitted rather in the style of the BR 'Standards' locomotive designs in a bid to ease maintenance.

This rebuild proved extremely successful and dramatically reduced the running costs of the locomotives and all the others in the class were similarly rebuilt by 1959. However by this time the Southern Region was moving forward with its plans for further electrification. The completion of the Chatham-Dover route reduced the work available to the class and consequently the first two, 35002 *Union Castle* and 35015 *Rotterdam Lloyd* were taken out of service in February 1964. By the following year almost half had been withdrawn and more were displaced by diesels when the Salisbury and Exeter section was transferred to the Western Region. Seven remained until the end of steam on the Southern on July 9 1967 when they were displaced from Southampton and Bournemouth duties by electric trains.

Healthy preservation

By this time the preservation movement was in full swing and the Bulleid engines were seen as good potential purchases

While the 'Merchants' were Southern Railway locomotives, 35019 *French Line CGT* was chosen to represent the design in British Railways Locomotive Exchanges in 1948. In May 1948 35019 departs the Eastern Region's London King's Cross terminus with a Leeds express. During the trials it was paired with a Stanier tender as the Southern Region tenders didn't have water scoops for refilling the tender tank on the move.
A.W. Croughton/Rail Archive Stephenson.

'MERCHANT NAVY' NUMBERING

SR number	BR number	Name
21C1	35001	Channel Packet
21C2	35002	Union Castle
21C3	35003	Royal Mail
21C4	35004	Cunard White Star
21C5	35005	Canadian Pacific
21C6	35006	Peninsular & Oriental S.N. Co.
21C7	35007	Aberdeen Commonwealth
21C8	35008	Orient Line
21C9	35009	Shaw Savill
21C10	35010	Blue Star
21C11	35011	General Steam Navigation
21C12	35012	United States Lines
21C13	35013	Blue Funnel
21C14	35014	Nederland Line
21C15	35015	Rotterdam Lloyd
21C16	35016	Elders Fyffes
21C17	35017	Belgian Marine
21C18	35018	British India Line
21C19	35019	French Line CGT
21C20	35020	Bibby Line
	35021	New Zealand Line
	35022	Holland America Line
	35023	Holland Afrika Line
	35024	East Asiatic Company
	35025	Brocklebank Line
	35026	Lamport & Holt Line
	35027	Port Line
	35028	Clan Line
	35029	Ellerman Lines
	35030	Elder Dempster Lines

Notes: Southern Railway numbers were only applied to 21C1-21C20. British Railways numbers were introduced from January 1948.

The driver of 21C13 *Blue Funnel* waits for the signal to clear at London Waterloo with the 'Devon Belle' in 1946. Note the smoke deflector mounted 'Devon Belle' board.

Lewis Coles/Rail Archive Stephenson.

due to them having been rebuilt relatively recently. A total of 11 eventually made it into private hands but so far only five have been in steam with the latest to return to working order being 35006 *Peninsular & Oriental S.N. Co* at the Gloucestershire Warwickshire Railway. Perhaps the most famous of these is 35028 *Clan Line* which has been a frequent main line performer over many years working regularly at the head of the British Pullman excursions from London on the former Southern Region.

One example, 35029 *Ellerman Lines*, has been seen by many thousands of people for it is exhibited in the Great Hall at the National Railway Museum in York where it has been sectioned so that visitors can better understand the workings of a steam engine. Many of the others will never run again because they are of limited use on today's heritage railways, being too powerful and heavy on fuel for conventional services. However, when on the main line 35005 *Canadian Pacific* and 35028 *Clan Line* have proved their potential time

and time again working specials.

Undoubtedly the 'Merchant Navy' was a trailblazing design that caught the public's imagination with its bold styling and attractive Malachite green colour scheme. Its engineering features were well thought out but unfortunately did not work as well in practice as they did on the drawing board.

The oil bath enclosed valve gear was a particular problem and for enginemen the steam reverser was a constant source of annoyance. On the positive side the boiler and cylinder arrangement could not be

faulted and the locomotives could always provide enough steam and power for the duties they were required to perform. Once modified they proved to be very fast, with one clocked at 105mph in 1967, and would undoubtedly have been capable of great feats had their service lives not been prematurely ended by modernisation.

The 'Merchant Navy' was one of the great passenger designs of all time and one that was a great credit to a designer who is perhaps somewhat underrated by enthusiasts today. Ⓗ

With the 'Bournemouth Belle' headboard on the front lamp iron 35011 *General Steam Navigation* passes Micheldever with the Up Pullman working in 1950. The train is formed of 12-wheel Pullman cars – a model previously produced by Hornby.

Frank Hebron/Rail Archive Stephenson.

Model Development

Creating a brand new model for the Hornby range with today's demands for accuracy and detail is a big project. Mike Wild meets the Hornby Development Team to find out exactly how a model goes from an idea to production.

10 STAGES OF MODEL PRODUCTION

1. Choose a project
2. Research
3. CAD/CAM design
4. Stereo engineering sample
5. First engineering sample
6. Second engineering sample
7. Artwork
8. Decorated sample
9. Production sample
10. Production and shipping

Opening the box of the latest locomotive from Hornby it's hard to appreciate just how much work has gone into producing it - but every part, every detail and every change has had to be researched thoroughly to put together the high quality product which today's model railway sector demands.

Hornby is well known for the quality of its products and these are brought together by the Hornby Development Team of eight people, each with their own responsibility in ensuring every new product is just as good, if not better, than what went before. The team has developed outstanding products ranging from glamorous express locomotives such as the unmistakable Gresley 'P2' 2-8-2

2001 *Cock O' the North* and British Railway's unique '8P' 4-6-2 71000 *Duke of Gloucester* through to humble goods locomotives such as the charming and antiquated Worsdell 'J15' 0-6-0 goods locomotive which made its debut in the first half of 2015.

There have been many more too – the Gresley 'A4', Bulleid 'West Country' and Stanier 'Duchess' class 'Pacifics' all spring to mind – and while steam is often the focus of attention Hornby is no stranger to diesel and electric locomotives with the exceptional detail of its Brush Class 60 still being regarded as one of its all-time greats.

We met with Product Development Manager Edd

Batchelor, Hornby Engineer Nick Scott and Researcher Paul Isles to learn about the process at Hornby's new headquarters in Kent. Set in a busy business centre the glass walled building hums with activity as the design teams for Hornby and its other businesses Airfix, Corgi and Scalextric all go about their work.

Starting blocks

One of the greatest challenges which faces the Hornby team is what to make next. We've all got our own ideas about what we think they should produce, but how do they actually go about making the selection for each new range? Researcher Paul Isles explains: "It's a combination. We

get requests, research potentials and look for logical developments. We get a lot of e-mails and we keep a close eye on the popular model railway forums too. Talking to people at shows gives us a good idea of what is popular and what is coming up as the next trend. Another important consideration is past performance. We've cut ourselves a niche in producing suburban and goods locomotives in recent years whereas once we were more focused on the prestigious express locomotives."

Of course that doesn't mean that express locomotives have been forgotten, but in today's model railway sector the vast majority

The Hornby Development Team is constantly producing new locomotives and rolling stock. To reach the final stage of production for a new steam locomotive like the GWR 'King' 4-6-0 can take up to 18 months.

have already been covered to a high standard. An exception though is the original condition Bulleid 'Merchant Navy' 4-6-2 which is joining Hornby's extensive range of Southern Railway/Region locomotives in 2016.

The ideal locomotive will have a long life, be a large class from which to choose examples to model, with livery changes and lots of names - but that isn't the be all and end all. For example, the Crosti '9F' 2-10-0 released as part of the RailRoad range in 2015 was an onward development of the BR Standard '9F' in the same section, but there were only 10 Crosti 2-10-0s and they only lasted in service for a maximum of 10 years.

Finding suitable subjects can be a challenge, particularly when it comes to express locomotives although one stood out for the 2016 range. "The 'Merchant Navy' is one of the last big express locomotives to be done for 'OO' and it's a big project too because of the number of variations which existed within the class. In fact in total there are 180 options with the 30 'Merchant Navy' locomotives when you take into account detail variations, liveries and major changes to the design," Paul explains. "It has been in our plans to produce the model for a long time, but it has taken until now for the time to be right to actually go ahead and make it."

All this has to be researched and once a project has been selected as having potential Paul steps in to begin a programme of research. Initially it starts with reading as Paul builds up a picture of why the locomotive was built, what it was used for and, if it changed, why it was modified. "The background is important as it helps us to understand the subject properly," Paul adds.

Sourcing plans is an important priority (although it isn't always possible) while books, photographs and contemporary reports are all used too. If a locomotive, carriage or wagon still exists and is accessible then the Hornby team

will head out for the day equipped with measuring equipment to record detailed measurements and particularly to establish the position of smaller components in relation to each other.

Laser scanning has also been used as a means of adding to the data pool on recent projects such as the Class 71 Bo-Bo electric for 2016 and the Adams '0415' 4-4-2T announced for the 2015 range, but it isn't seen as a catch all by the Hornby Development Team. Paul explains: "3D scanning is great, but you only get what is in front of you and in some cases that isn't enough. For example, ☞

if we were starting again on the streamlined Stanier 'Duchess' we could go to the National Railway Museum and seek permission to scan 6229 *Duchess of Hamilton*, but the data would be wrong as the casing is narrower and lower because it was built to operate within the current British loading gauge which is smaller than that of the steam era."

The Class 71 was scanned for confirmation partly because none of the original detailed drawings for the locomotive exist with only basic engineering outlines of the locomotive available. This was helpful in establishing its shape.

With the basics done Hornby then starts investigating what it can physically do and how it can be tooled and Paul has to understand how the design team thinks so that he can make proposals which are within the technical abilities of production and assembly. A design brief is

Wire frame drawings give the designers an insight into the available space inside a model's shell for motors and drive trains.

With CAD drawing work complete the first physical version of the model is a rapid prototype created using 3D printing technology. This allows the designers to assess the basic shape of the model and how it interacts with the chassis before committing to the expensive stage of hard steel tooling.

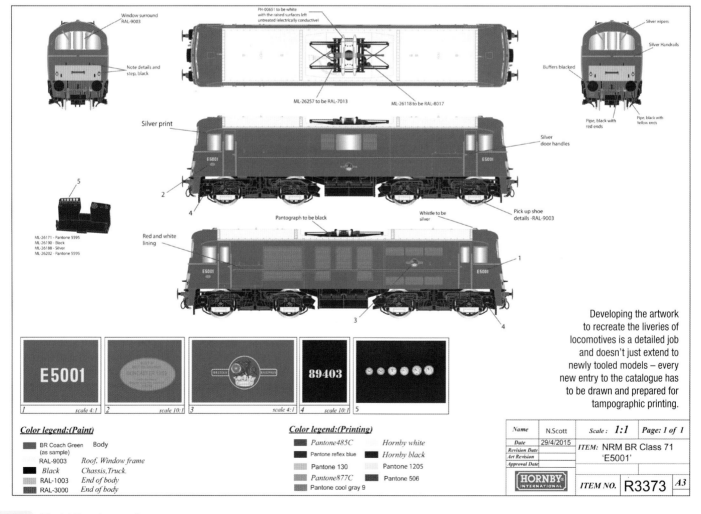

Developing the artwork to recreate the liveries of locomotives is a detailed job and doesn't just extend to newly tooled models – every new entry to the catalogue has to be drawn and prepared for tampographic printing.

Color legend:(Paint)

BR Coach Green (as sample)	Body
RAL-9003	*Roof, Window frame*
Black	*Chassis, Truck.*
RAL-1003	*End of body*
RAL-3000	*End of body*

Color legend:(Printing)

Pantone485C	*Hornby white*
Pantone reflex blue	*Hornby black*
Pantone 130	Pantone 1205
Pantone877C	Pantone 506
Pantone cool gray 9	

Name	N.Scott	Scale :	*1:1*	Page: 1 of 1
Date	29/4/2015			
Revision Date		*ITEM:* NRM BR Class 71		
Art Revision		'E5001'		
Approval Date				
HORNBY INTERNATIONAL		*ITEM NO.*	R3373	A3

prepared and handed over to Edd and Nick so that it can be discussed from both a market and technical perspective. Not all projects get through this stage and some will be postponed until the time is right, but others go straight through to the next stage and the start of design work.

Model design

With a project approved for the next phase one of the three designers – Phil Morley, Carl Hart or Steve Merry – is selected to take it on and Paul remains on hand to assist with finding further information as the design process unfolds. This is done using Computer Aided Design (CAD) software.

Product Development Manager Edd Batchelor takes over: "One designer is allocated to each project and they see that through from start to finish. It will take around four to five months to design a locomotive, but a wagon can be drawn up in as little as a month. A single carriage can take quite some time, whereas developing a rake of four can take as little as three or four months."

The designer starts by looking through the research and finding the main variations. "In big classes we will concentrate on the main variations," Edd continues, "but for small classes we will consider doing all the possible variations."

The physical process of designing the model starts with the chassis. This is laid out with accurate dimensions for the wheelbase which are taken from plans wherever possible. Chief Engineer Nick Scott adds: "We have to make adjustments here and there to wheel profiles so that the models will actually run on the track, but they are so small you would never notice."

With the chassis established the motor and geartrain are designed next. Five-pole motors are now being used throughout the main range, but Hornby has a catalogue of eight which can be used to suit different locomotive sizes and types. These are of two formats: one which uses rare earth magnets and one which

Design of the models is handled by a team of skilled engineers using a Computer Aided Design (CAD) programme. Here Carl Hart continues development on the new 'Merchant Navy' for 2016.

uses moulded magnets. The latter offers lower torque, but they are cheaper to produce.

Motor selection is made to suit individual locomotives while the geartrain, which uses a range of standard components, is also designed new for each model. The designer also has to consider balancing to ensure that it has adequate traction, much as with a real locomotive.

Once the chassis is complete up to the drivetrain the detailed

and painstaking work of generating the body begins. This is where the time goes as the designers work closely with the research material and drawings to ensure that all the profiles, shapes and curves accurately reflect the prototype. The first choice of materials for manufacture are ABS and polystyrene plastics, but die-casting has been used in some smaller locomotives including the 'J15', '700' and 'D16' which all have metal boilers. This material is

used where space is at a premium to introduce adhesive weight to the model for traction purposes.

A change in recent years is that even where a tender design already exists from a previous model it will be created fresh to go with new projects. For example, while the 'B17', 'D16' and 'B12' all share a common short wheelbase Great Eastern Railway style tender, each model has its own set of tools for the tender to ensure that the whole locomotive is kept 👉

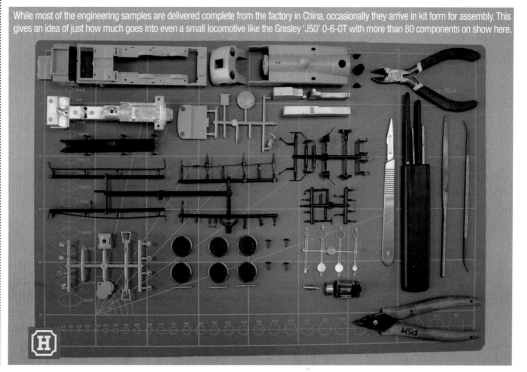

While most of the engineering samples are delivered complete from the factory in China, occasionally they arrive in kit form for assembly. This gives an idea of just how much goes into even a small locomotive like the Gresley 'J50' 0-6-0T with more than 80 components on show here.

Research is essential and it comes in many forms. Photographs, drawings, reports and measurements all go together to create the final package.

together in one suite. Nick Scott commented: "It is more expensive doing it this way, but it gives us security in knowing that all the elements are together and reduces delays in manufacture."

Sampling

Once the design work is complete a set of 3D printed parts are ordered and the chassis and mechanism are assembled to prove the design mechanically. This is an important stage in the process which happens before any of the expensive metal cutting for tooling work begins. At the same time the CAD files and

data are sent over to Hornby's vendors in China for quotes to be produced for production.

The 3D printed bodyshell is assembled to a complete running chassis which is then checked to make sure it goes through points and curves and that none of the wheels clash with one another. Edd: "This is the time to put things right in the CAD file before we commit to the tools."

With the quotes in and a vendor for manufacture selected the next phase is tackled in China where the vendor takes blocks of metal and cuts them to produce specialised hard steel tools which

are then used to injection mould the finely detailed components of the model. This is a highly skilled part of the process which is handled by a mixture of Computer Aided Manufacturing (CAM) and hand working to develop a fully detailed set of metal moulds.

The first shots from this brand new tool are produced within around 10 weeks which comes as a kit of parts to show what the tooling is capable of making. At the same time a first complete engineering sample of the model is delivered which includes a fully working chassis and a fully assembled body. Occasionally

these samples are assembled in the Hornby offices, but more often than not they arrive fully assembled from the vendor.

This sample is then fully assessed for running and detail by the Hornby Development Team before being painted in a base colour for the main liveries so it can be used as the basis for artwork on the packaging.

Any adjustments to the design, tools and assembly process that are necessary are highlighted and this leads on to a second engineering sample. At the same time the Hornby Design Team completes the packaging artwork

The CAD drawings allow a full detailed 3D computer model of the planned locomotive to be drawn. Components can be adjusted, moved or even removed to allow the inner workings to be seen. This is the CAD drawing for the new 'B12' 4-6-0 for release in 2016.

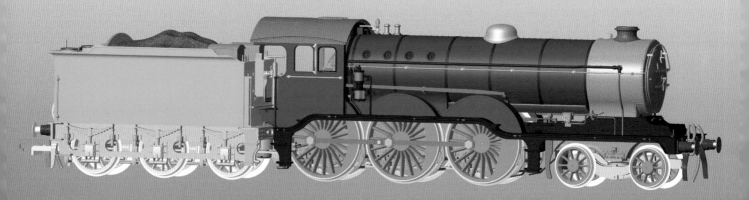

Engineering prototypes of the model are produced and inspected in detail by the development team to check for accuracy and performance. Running qualities are checked carefully at this stage and any final amendments can be made.

out on arrival from China. Tests of Electro Magnetic Compatibility (EMC) have to be passed in Hong Kong too before full production can be authorised and this is one of the reasons why Hornby's models have lots of electrical pick-ups.

The physical production process isn't mechanised with much of the assembly being done by hand. Edd commented: "There are lots of components which can be mass produced, but in a lot of cases we are only making runs of 700-1,000 models at a time which means lots of hand finishing is required to put them together."

Production complete and models approved, it then takes four to five weeks

for the full shipment to travel by sea from China to the UK for distributing by the Hersden site to its retailer network, keeping its customers happy.

It will have taken in the region of 18 months from the start of design work for a new locomotive to reach the stage where it arrives in the shops - and that isn't including the research which takes place beforehand. It is a fascinating process and one which the Hornby Design Team takes in its stride every day with multiple projects on the go. The results are models to be proud of and products which we eagerly anticipate arriving in the shops. ⊞

HAVE YOUR SAY...

If you have an idea for a model which you think the Hornby range shouldn't be without write to *newclubs@hornby.com*

and delivers it to the vendor for printing keeping the ball rolling between the two sides of the world.

Leading into the final stages of development the Chinese vendor is supplied with artwork for the model's livery which is then turned into a set of tampographic printing slides which are used, literally, to print the lining, crests, numbers and other details onto the locomotive. In some cases this can get complex with multiple passes being required through the tampographic machine to achieve such detailed effects as full three colour BR mixed traffic lining and the detailed shading of pre-nationalisation lettering such as Southern 'sunshine' styles and the gold leaf shading used by the London North Eastern Railway.

The final phase

With all this done a decorated sample is sent back to the development team for scrutiny which leads onto a final sample being delivered as a complete item, fully packaged as it would come off the production line. If this is approved it is sent to Hornby's Hersden site for quality control analysis allowing testing of the production models to be carried

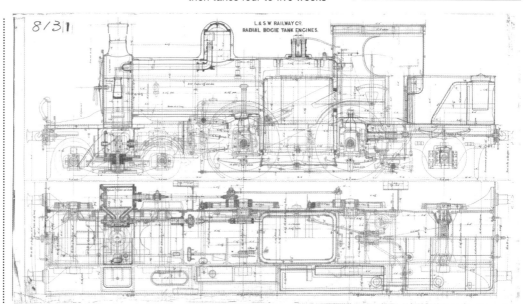

Works drawings offer a great deal of technical information, but where a locomotive exists a site visit will be made to double check measurements.

The chassis is the first part of a locomotive to be laid out in a CAD design programme – this provides the essential reference points for drawing the body.

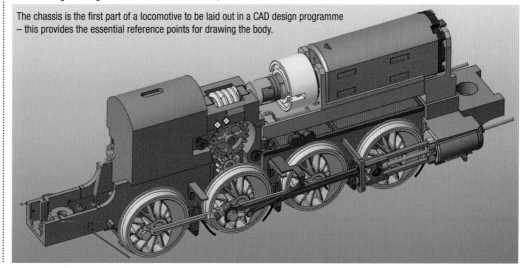

Planning
your first Railway

Knowing where to start can be the hardest part of beginning a new model railway project. Mike Wild highlights the key factors you need to know for a bright future in railway modelling.

Branch line layouts are a great way to replicate real railway operations more accurately as trains are shorter and stations are smaller. They lend themselves to realistic home layouts.
John Wiffen/*Hornby Magazine*.

Where do you start? What do you need? How big? Where to keep it? There are a lot of questions to be answered when starting out with designing and planning your first model railway, but most important of all is to enjoy it.

This hobby is a wonderful pastime. The quality and variety of today's mass-produced railway models are beyond anything modellers could have imagined, even into the 1990s, and that has brought an increasingly high standard of layouts to the fore as modellers move from building the rolling stock to creating an ever more detailed scene in which to run them.

Everyone has to start somewhere – nobody can achieve the pinnacle of greatness in a first project, although I'm sure I thought differently when I was building my first layout! – and it takes time to get off the ground and up and running. That is part of the joy - building a collection, acquiring new ideas and developing a model railway that will keep you entertained for years to come.

Don't be afraid to get started. The Hornby range includes a variety of train sets which are a perfect way of starting on the path to a model railway with all the basic ingredients you need to create a working railway in one box. Track, controller and train are all there and as they use Hornby's standard range of sectional track, it is a simple process to expand upon

this. The Hornby Trak Mat supplied with each train set provides ideas for moving on from that first simple circuit while keeping you within the boundaries of a set format.

With time and confidence you will want to develop your layout further and that means moving forward to consider where a layout might be housed permanently within the home or perhaps you will want to create a portable layout that can be stored away when not in use. Both are totally possible and through this Hornby Handbook we will be showing you skills for railway modelling to help you understand more about the hobby and to make your layouts even more detailed.

A home for your layout

Imagine you have your first train set. You've tried it out on the dining room table, altered track formations and dabbled with the potential of a model railway. Where do you go next? Most important now is to decide where the layout will be housed and there are four main places in the average home which hold potential: a spare room, a garage, a garden shed or the loft. If you are blessed with outbuildings then you have a great fifth option.

In the house – Inside the home is really the best place for a model railway, but only if you have space. There are several potential spaces which could be used for a model railway, but it all depends on what you want from your living space. A spare room could be used for a permanent layout with (☞

Building a model railway is a great pastime. This is Hornby Junction built by the Epsom and Ewell Model Railway Club which uses Hornby track, buildings, trains and more to recreate the world in miniature. Chris Nevard/*Hornby Magazine*.

even an 8ft x 6ft space offering ample opportunities for a cleverly designed layout. You could even build in storage and a workbench to suit the railway if you have the freedom to use a room solely for the railway. If you don't have a whole room available then consider wall mounting it in 'shelf' style so that the room can have multiple uses.

If a permanent layout isn't possible don't despair as it is quite feasible, with thought and planning, to develop a portable layout which can be stored away when out of use. I have seen elaborate systems in the past with layouts hinged from walls, on runners under beds and even on pulley systems from the roof – the latter though needs more than the average skill set to develop a safe and sturdy means of suspending a model when it is out of use.

Another way of creating a portable layout is to build a set of smaller baseboards which can be bolted together during use and then packed away neatly in a cupboard or corner of the room when not required.

Garage – While once the garage was the preserve of vehicle parking, today it is relatively rare to see garages used for their original purpose. Many have been converted into extra rooms or are used for storage. For the keen model railway builder the garage holds great potential. The average single garage has a floor space

When starting out mocking up ideas is a great way to find out what will work and what won't. This 4ft 6in x 4ft single board layout ultimately featured a small station with a single track goods yards. *Peter Marriott/Hornby Magazine.*

measuring roughly 16ft x 8ft while a double garage can be as large as 20ft x 20ft. That's a big space.

There are a few things to consider when choosing the garage as the home of your layout, however. Firstly, if it has a concrete floor, paint it! Concrete floors constantly create dust and that won't do a model railway any good at all. Secondly, make sure the doors are secure and invest in insulation to stop draughts and moisture from getting in.

These are the basics, but to make a garage 100% suitable for a permanent model railway ideally means adding some form of

insulation and plasterboard walling to reduce the effect of temperature changes. Some have gone to the lengths of fully converting a garage solely for the purpose of a model railway. Planning permission is not normally needed for garage conversions, but it is always wise to check with your local planning authority before committing to any work on your property.

Garden shed – The garden shed can be a cost effective way of creating extra space to house a model railway. Timber sheds are available in a variety of sizes ranging from 6ft x 4ft upwards. There are limitations to the type

of garden building which can be built without planning permission and these are detailed on *planningportal.gov.uk*.

If you select a garden shed there are several considerations. Firstly it will need a level concrete base on which to stand. Second, it will need to be watertight and the timber will need treating regularly to keep it in good condition. Internally, once you have assembled the building it will need lining with insulation and with plasterboard or timber cladding to make it habitable both for yourself and the railway. Mains power – which should only be handled by a qualified electrician – will also need

Support structures

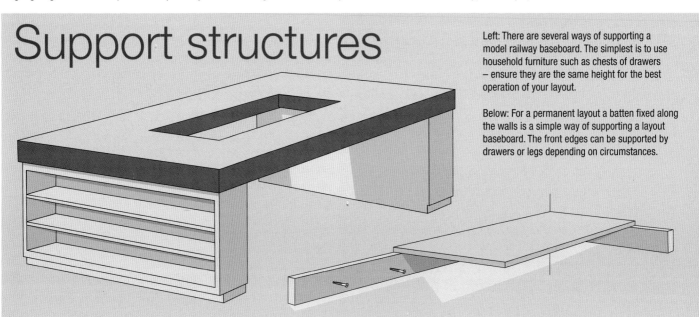

Left: There are several ways of supporting a model railway baseboard. The simplest is to use household furniture such as chests of drawers – ensure they are the same height for the best operation of your layout.

Below: For a permanent layout a batten fixed along the walls is a simple way of supporting a layout baseboard. The front edges can be supported by drawers or legs depending on circumstances.

adding to the shed so that you can operate your layout. A heater will also more than likely be needed.

However, once you have a garden shed you have an open space available to build what you like. The completed layout could even be extended to run out into the garden.

Loft – Of all the options on the table this is the most expensive and complex, but the result can be a really useful and large space for a model railway. Any conversion or use of a loft space for anything other than storage will need planning permission and involvement from Building Regulations as it affects the structure of a property. The loft ☞

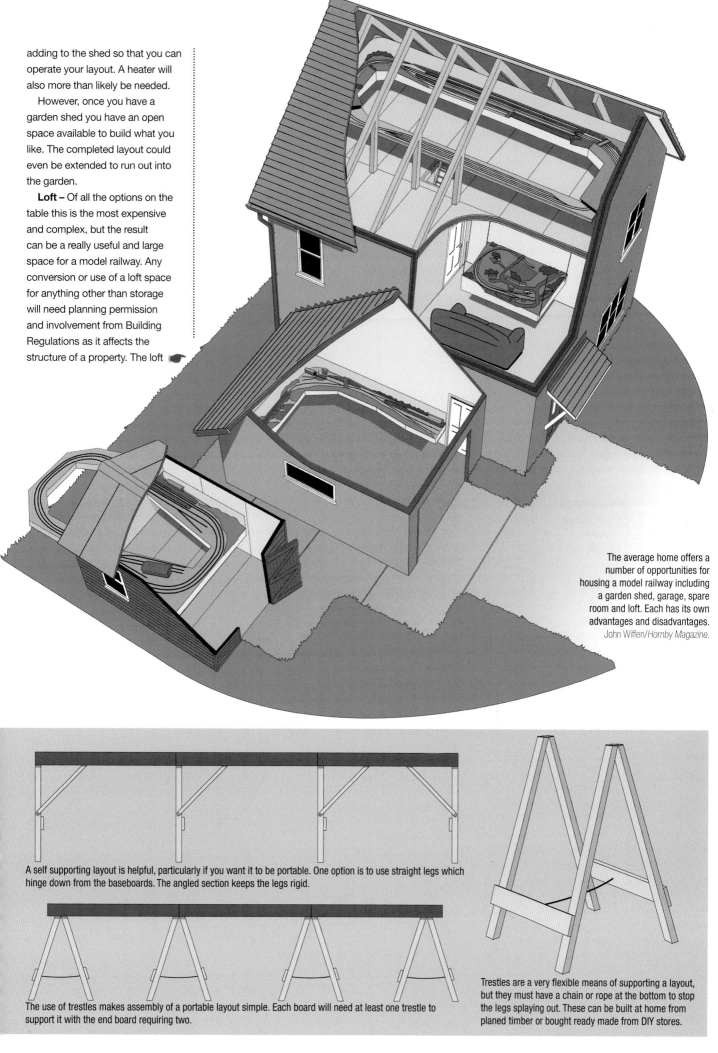

The average home offers a number of opportunities for housing a model railway including a garden shed, garage, spare room and loft. Each has its own advantages and disadvantages.
John Wiffen/Hornby Magazine.

A self supporting layout is helpful, particularly if you want it to be portable. One option is to use straight legs which hinge down from the baseboards. The angled section keeps the legs rigid.

The use of trestles makes assembly of a portable layout simple. Each board will need at least one trestle to support it with the end board requiring two.

Trestles are a very flexible means of supporting a layout, but they must have a chain or rope at the bottom to stop the legs splaying out. These can be built at home from planed timber or bought ready made from DIY stores.

does offer a good space, but cost will put most off using this area of the house.

Layout styles

While you are thinking about where your layout will go it's time to start plotting the type of layout you want to build. Do you simply want to expand on the train set concept keeping the layout down to a suitable size or are you looking to recreate a small part of the real railway system in miniature?

There are infinite choices. Do you create a freelance design or model a real location? A freelance model based on a fictional location will get much quicker results as buildings can be selected to suit your personal tastes rather than replicating exact structures. That is not to say that you can't replicate a real location - far from it - but that it takes much more time to research a prototype and then create scale models of the buildings which surround the railway.

You might not want a scenic layout at all and there is nothing wrong with establishing a model railway which can be assembled and dismantled using sectional track for the pure enjoyment of running trains. It is your layout and you can

TOP TIPS

1 Get started! Train sets are the ideal place to begin a first journey into model railways.

2 Look for a space in the home first – it is the most cost effective way of making space for a layout.

3 Sketch out ideas and try layout planning software like Track Master to see what might work.

4 Don't jump in too fast – building London King's Cross as your first layout isn't necessarily the best way forward!

5 A continuous run layout with two tracks is an ideal starter project – it keeps trains moving.

6 Consider a portable layout if you don't have space for a permanent model.

7 No space is too small for a working railway – even a box file can be used to create a working layout.

8 Build your confidence by adding sectional track pieces to develop a train set.

9 Join a local model railway club for ideas, support and to learn new skills.

10 If you are planning to modify part of your house and build a shed check on the regulations at *planningportal.gov.uk*

run and build it how you like.

Permanent layouts are by far the simplest to build as there is no need to consider the additional wiring or woodwork involved in creating a portable layout. Permanent layouts can be built into a room like a piece of furniture allowing the space beneath to be kept free for storage.

A portable layout is more tricky to build as it will require a set of baseboards which can be dismantled for storage or transport. This type of layout is most suited to those looking to attend model railway exhibitions where the model will need to be packed into a car or van carefully for its journey. The upside of creating a portable layout, even if it never leaves home, is that your hard work won't be lost if you have to move.

Within these two types of layout design there are a number of options. If you are short on space but want a realistic layout then a branch line scene with short trains and compact stations might be an ideal choice, while if you have a greater area available then a main

line will be an attractive idea.

Branch lines tend to be single track working on the 'one engine in steam' principle while main line scenes usually have at least a double track main line meaning that at least two trains can be on the move at any one time. Main lines also give scope to run a wider range of motive power in a realistic setting and especially the more glamorous 'Pacifics' and named engines or high speed trains like the Class 43 HST or Pendolino.

The most common type of layout is the continuous run where trains are able to circulate continuously. This can be a single or double track – or more – and allows trains to be run freely. Home layouts, like exhibition layouts, can benefit from an off-scene storage area where trains are parked to represent the rest of the world, increasing the number of trains available to the modeller.

Terminus layouts are more suited to the avid modeller as they don't allow trains to be left running. Each will need controlling to travel from its storage area to the terminus, but that terminus could range in size from a single platform branch line affair right through to a model of a busy station with multiple platforms, locomotive depot, goods yards and more.

If you have more space available then a double track main line running around the room with offer a great deal of operational value. This idea features a high level station with a quarry site set below ground level. *John Wiffen/ Hornby Magazine.*

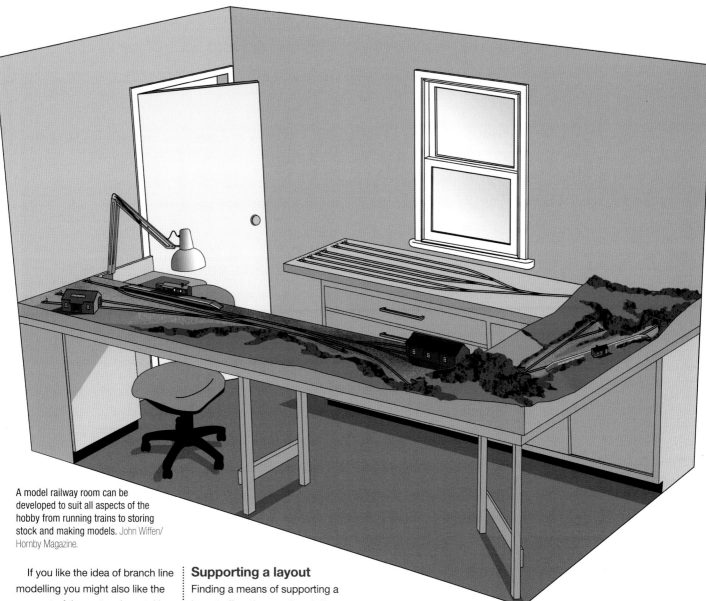

A model railway room can be developed to suit all aspects of the hobby from running trains to storing stock and making models. *John Wiffen/ Hornby Magazine.*

If you like the idea of branch line modelling you might also like the concept of the system layout. Here trains emerge from a storage yard representing the rest of the world and travel around a room passing through a station on the way to their destination at a terminus. It's a step up from the straightforward terminus station arrangement as it means more features and stations can be built. This doesn't have to be on a branch line basis, but most homes don't offer the space needed to create a main line system layout.

In British modelling single deck layouts are by far the most popular, but in America multi-deck layouts are quite common, allowing much more railway to be built in a relatively small area. Different scenes can be built on different levels but care will need to be taken to develop gradients which don't bring trains to a standstill. Planning and research here is essential.

Supporting a layout

Finding a means of supporting a layout offers three main solutions which will suit different styles of model. The simplest method of supporting a baseboard is to use household furniture such as chests of drawers. So long as all units are the same height they will provide a firm and solid base on which a board can be rested.

The second solution is to use separate legs. These could be vertical straight legs which support individual corners or, for a portable layout, trestles which form a strong triangular shape. Legs of both styles can be made from readily available planed timber using screws and glue to create strong rigid joins.

The third option, which needs to be used in conjunction with either furniture or separate legs, is to create a wall mounted bracket to support the rear edge of the baseboard. This can be as simple as a batten fixed to the wall with

screws which will then require either legs or furniture to be used to support the front edge of the layout. This is ideal where a layout is to be permanently housed in the corner of a room as two edges of the baseboard can be supported by wall mounted battens – you need confidence with an electric drill to do this though.

No space, no problem

But what if you really haven't got space to build your own model railway? Then why not consider joining a local model railway club? More than likely they will have projects and working layouts to get involved in and it is a great environment in which to learn new skills and develop your own ideas for when the time comes to build your own layout. They can be great social fun too while the annual exhibition hosted by local

clubs will be full of inspiration when other likeminded layout owners come together to showcase their projects.

Designing a model railway is a very rewarding and enjoyable process and one which when done with knowledge of the basics will result in a smooth running and interesting project. The features in this Handbook will show you how to build a simple baseboard, how to lay track and how to move into other aspects of railway modelling such as scenery and detailing. If you are looking for more knowledge check out the Hornby Forums where you can exchange ideas and gather feedback on your model plans.

Once you are on the right track I guarantee you will be hooked! There is so much to learn and enjoy and it all starts with a humble train set. Ⓗ

Baseboards
for beginners

TOOLS

- Handsaw
- Pencil
- Tape measure
- Tri-square
- Electric screwdriver

A solid level base is an important part of any successful model railway. With many options to choose from, Mike Wild shows one method for creating strong, light boards.

There are many choices when it comes to providing a baseboard for a model railway. At the simplest end of the scale you could use 18mm thick plywood or chipboard supported by chests of drawers.

For this method a single sheet of 8ft x 4ft timber will provide ample space to put together a train set style layout using the four available curve radii produced by Hornby – see pages 38-43 for more on track – but it can be difficult to transport and manoeuvre such a large piece of sheet timber.

To create a long lasting layout base then a good move forward from the solid sheet route is to look at producing simple baseboards with a timber frame. Thinner and lighter sheet material can be used for the top and multiples can be built to create a layout of nearly any size or shape. My own personal preference is to use baseboards measuring 4ft x 2ft – you can get enough from a single sheet of 8ft x 4ft sheet timber to create four board tops – and with a planed timber frame they are light and strong and provide ample space for housing point motors and wiring out of sight. A means of supporting these boards is required which could

include using household furniture or creating sets of supporting legs.

The method shown here is tried and tested and only requires a basic toolkit to complete. There is no fancy woodwork here – just basic butt joints to create the frame. However, if you feel that building baseboards is beyond your skills, don't be put off railway modelling as there are a number of companies which will produce bespoke baseboards to suit your needs including White Rose Model Works, Elite Baseboards and Model Railway Solutions.

The method shown here uses 69mm x 18mm planed timber for the frame and 9mm thick plywood for the surface. Two types of screws are used – 4.0 x 30mm screws to secure the frame together and the top to the frame and 4.0 x 20mm screws to fit 6mm MDF backscene panels to the boards.

The following step by step guide shows how we build baseboards.

A solid baseboard is an important foundation for a successful model railway. Plywood is an ideal material for a baseboard top as it is both strong and light.

WHAT WE USED

- 9mm plywood, cut to 4ft x 2ft size at DIY store for baseboard top
- 69mm x 18mm planed timber, 2.4m lengths – two per 4ft x 2ft baseboard
- 4.0 x 30mm twin thread wood screws
- M6 50mm bolts, M6 wing nuts, M6 oversize 30mm washers

STEP **BY** STEP BUILDING A TIMBER FRAMED SOLID TOP BASEBOARD

STEP 1
The materials for this project to build a pair of 4ft x 2ft baseboards consist of two pieces of 9mm plywood cut to size (4ft x 2ft) at a DIY store, four 2.4m lengths of 69mm x 18mm planed timber, 4.0 x 30mm wood screws.

STEP 2
Only a basic toolkit is needed to build a baseboard. It consists of an electric screwdriver, a handsaw, pencil, tape measure and a tri-square. A sturdy workbench is useful to support lengths of timber during cutting.

STEP 3
With the length of the baseboards established as 4ft, the first job is to mark out lengths of timber to create the long sides. Using a tape measure and tri-square, 4ft is marked accurately onto the timber. Remember, measure twice, cut once.

STEP 4
You don't need fancy electric saws for this job – a handsaw with sharp teeth will make easy (and neater) work of the planed timber. Follow the line carefully. For greater accuracy a mitre box and saw can be used for this job.

STEP 5
Knowing the lengths of each piece of timber is helpful. We mark the lengths onto each piece in pencil and because each baseboard is a standard size they can be used as the frame for any board.

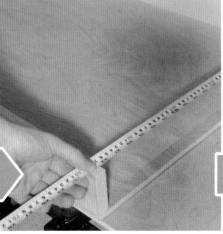

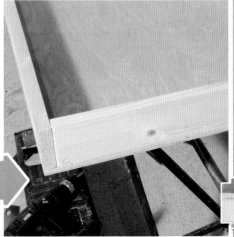

STEP 6
This is where a power tool is very useful – inserting screws. The heads of these 30mm screws create their own countersunk hole as they are driven into the plywood. An electric screwdriver makes this a quick process. Insert screws roughly every 6in-9in along the edge of the board.

STEP 7
With the long sides fixed in place we can now cut the end and cross brace pieces. Using a tape measure, carefully measure the distance between the two sides of the frame and then transfer those measures to planed timber for cutting.

STEP 8
Having cut the end panel for the frame, it is pressed into place. It should be a snug fit between the sides.

STEP 9
Using a pair of 4.0 x 30mm wood screws the end is fixed to the sides. A bead of PVA glue was also run down each frame joint for increased strength.

STEP 10
Cross braces are essential for a strong and rigid baseboard. In a 4ft x 2ft baseboard we add two braces set 15in from each end. They are fixed in place to the frame with beads of PVA glue and 30mm wood screws.

STEP 11
One of the advantages of a framed baseboard is that electrical wiring can be hidden out of sight, but it will need a route to pass through the frame. Drilling holes through the cross braces is easier at this stage than when track and scenery are on top.

STEP 12
The completed baseboard has had additional screws inserted around the edge to hold each section of the frame securely to the baseboard top. Note the pencil marks for the cross braces to allow easy positioning of screws through the top to fix it to these frame members.

STEP 13
We want to join the two 4ft x 2ft boards together to create a layout measuring 8ft x 2ft. To do this the boards need to be clamped together firmly with the upper surface absolutely in line.

STEP 14
With the frames clamped together and the position checked for accuracy, a 6.5mm drill is used to create two holes through the baseboard frame ends. These holes are then used to place M6 (6mm diameter) coach bolts through the two frame ends to bolt them together. Matching M6 wing nuts and oversize 30mm washers are used.

STEP 15
As a final step we painted each of the two baseboards in grey using household emulsion paints. This seals the wood and provides a neat coloured base for future modelling work. The boards are now ready to be developed into a scenic model railway.

Laying down the line

To get the best from Hornby's range of outstanding models means laying track. Ian Goodman explains how to use Hornby's set and flexible systems to create a smooth running railway.

Using express points and semi-flexible track this station scene has been laid out using Hornby components. The track has been laid on strips of cork underlay to assist in quiet running and creating a realistic look to the track later in the modelling process.

TOOLS

- Craft knife
- Pin hammer
- Pliers
- Junior hacksaw or multi-tool mini drill
- Pin vice
- 1mm drill bit
- 5mm drill bit

Railways wouldn't exist without track and it is the same when it comes to models. Hornby produces all the components that you need to get started in building anything from a small shunting layout right through to the biggest and most complex station projects you can think of.

There are two distinct groups of track in the Hornby portfolio: sectional track and its two types of flexible track. Sectional track is what you will find in train sets

and track packs and it is a range of track components produced to specific lengths and curves which can be joined together to create an operating railway in a matter of minutes. Accurate alignment of the metal rail joiners is essential for smooth running.

Within the sectional track range (see Diagram 1) are curves in four radii, allowing up to four tracks to be laid, one outside the other, to create a busy main line layout. Added to this there are four lengths of straight, two lengths of point in left and right-hand formats, curved points, diamond crossings, power tracks, isolating tracks and more.

Where smooth or shallow curves are wanted then Hornby's flexible or semi-flexible track can be used. These two types of track are supplied in yard lengths which can be cut to length to suit specific locations and formed to any curve you can imagine within the capabilities of the models

which will run on them. It allows wider radius curves than those in the sectional track range to be reproduced more accurately reflecting the real railway.

An important factor to consider for a permanent model railway on a wooden baseboard is vibrations from passing trains. These can be dampened with Hornby's foam underlay strip which is pre-moulded to match the arrangement of the sleepers on its track, combined with underlay sheets which can be used under points and accessories. Another option if you are seeking detail is to use cork sheet which can be cut back to the width of the track allowing a realistic ballast 'shoulder' to be created – see pages 80-83 for more on ballasting – using loose ballasting methods.

The step by step guides show how to work with sectional track and how a more complex track arrangement has been created for the station project. ☞

WHAT WE USED - THE CIRCLE

Product	Cat No.	Quantity
Third radius double curve	R609	8
Third radius curve	R608	1
Short straight	R610	1
Left-hand curved point	R8074	1
'Y' point	R8076	1
Straight	R600	1
Power track	R8206	1
Track pins	R207	1

STEP **BY** STEP 🖌 THE CIRCLE PROJECT

STEP 1

To demonstrate how simple it is to set up a circuit of sectional Hornby track we mocked up a 4ft x 4ft circuit with a three points to create two versions of the plan – one simple and one with a small twist to make it more interesting. First, all the components were laid out in place to make sure everything would fit together.

STEP 2

Each piece of Hornby sectional track is pre-fitted with metal rail joiners on the left-hand rail so that when two parts are brought together the rail joiners slide onto the bare rail on the adjoining piece of track. Here we have a curved point and two sections of curved plain track.

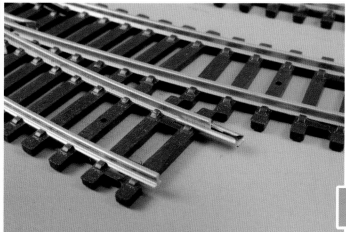

STEP 3

Seen close-up the design of the rail joiner is clear. It has an opening in the centre shaped to match the rail profile and is a tight fit onto the next section. This joiner aligns the track and transmits power so a snug fit is essential.

STEP 4

To join two pieces of track a smooth and level surface is advisable. Bring the two parts together and locate the bare rail ends into the rail joiners on the others. Gently start the process of pushing the parts together ensure that the rails sit inside the joiners.

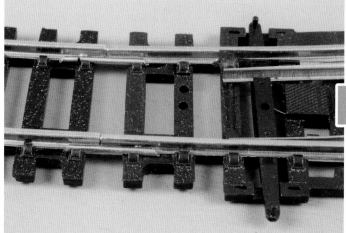

STEP 5

Once you are happy with the position push the two track sections together fully so the rails butt up against each other. Each piece of track needs to be treated in the same way to create the track plan for the 'circle'.

STEP 6

Putting power to the rails calls for the addition of a power track. This straight piece of track is equipped with a connector which can either be used in conjunction with the power lead supplied in train sets or a pair of suitable wires. Here 16/0.2 figure of eight cable has been used to link the power track with the controller.

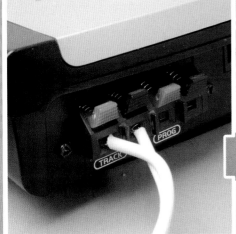

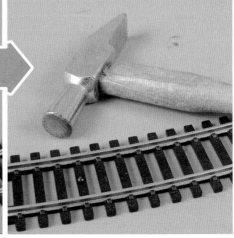

STEP 7

The other end of the wires from the power track can then be connected to the track connection terminals on your controller. This is the Hornby Elite Digital Command Control unit which has the track connections clearly labelled.

STEP 8

For a permanent layout the track needs to be pinned to the baseboard for the best performance of locomotives and rolling stock. This keeps the track together and stops it from moving out of place. To do this we used Hornby track pins (R207).

STEP 9

To insert the track pins first use a pair of pliers to position the pin in the pre-drilled hole in the sleeper web. Use firm pressure to press the tip of the pin into the wood below. To complete the job use a pin hammer to tap the pin fully home to that it holds the track against the baseboard surface.

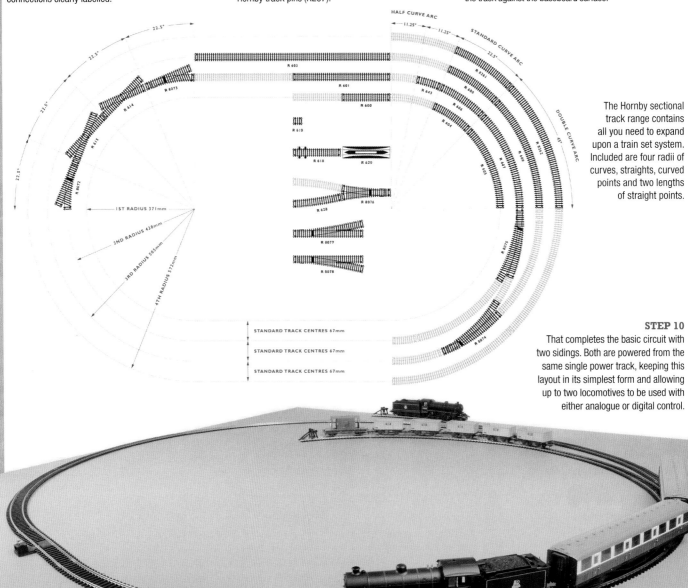

The Hornby sectional track range contains all you need to expand upon a train set system. Included are four radii of curves, straights, curved points and two lengths of straight points.

STEP 10

That completes the basic circuit with two sidings. Both are powered from the same single power track, keeping this layout in its simplest form and allowing up to two locomotives to be used with either analogue or digital control.

Flexible and semi-flexible track allows more realistic track formations to be created. The track can be gently curved to suit different configurations beyond the scope of the sectional track system.

LAYING FLEXIBLE TRACK FOR THE 'STATION' PROJECT

STEP BY STEP — THE STATION

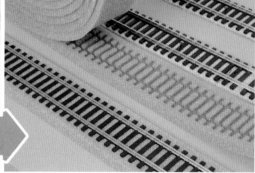

STEP 1
Moving to the bigger project for this handbook, we developed a layout plan for a country station with a small locomotive shed which uses semi-flexible track (R8090) together with express points. Flexible and semi-flexible track allows the flowing curves of the real railway to be more accurately recreated.

STEP 2
There are a number of options for underlay to go beneath the track which will help soften the sound of trains running on hard wooden baseboards. Two of the most popular are foam (R638) and cork sheet, which is available from model shops. Foam comes on a roll with moulded spaces for sleepers while cork needs to be cut to shape to suit the track formation.

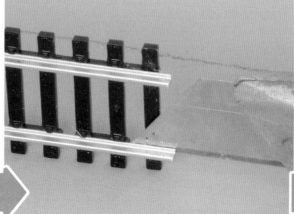

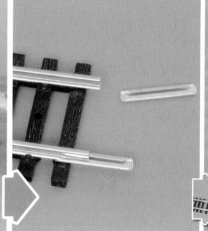

STEP 3
With a view to creating realistic ballast 'shoulder' on this country station project we elected to use cork sheet for the underlay. Our choice is 1/16in thick and supplied on a roll which can be laid underneath the track.

STEP 4
Using semi-flexible track throws up another small job – joining sections together. Unlike sectional track, flexible tracks are supplied without rail joiners fitted so you will need to fit your own. To do this means either removing the first sleeper from the end of the section or, as here, cutting the rail chair off the sleeper so that a rail joiner can slide onto the rail end between the sleeper and the rail.

STEP 5
With the chair removed a metal rail joiner (R910) can be pushed onto the end of each rail and it will sit neatly above the sleeper.

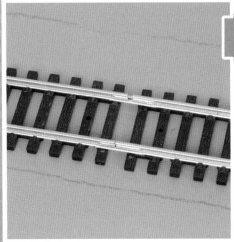

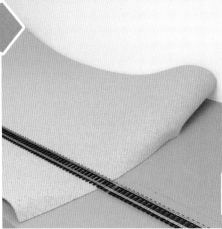

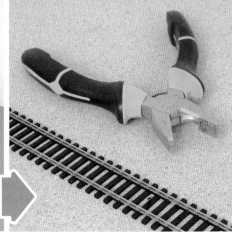

STEP 6

Having repeated the cutting process on the next section of track the two can be pushed together in the same manner as sectional track. Ensure that the rails are fully home in the joiners for smooth train operation.

STEP 7

Next the cork sheet is laid out on the baseboard surface. We had already pre-marked the position of the main running lines through this station scene in pencil.

STEP 8

The track can now be pinned lightly to the cork using track pins (R207) to secure both the track and cork to the board. These are pushed partway into the baseboard surface with a pair of pliers, allowing for easy adjustment if required.

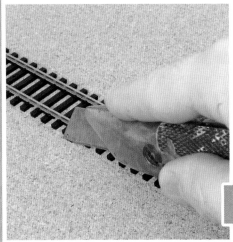

STEP 9

With the track holding the cork in place a craft knife with a sharp blade is used to cut away the excess cork from around the track. Use a low angle with the blade to avoid ripping the cork surface.

STEP 10

Once the cork has been cut away from the running line it leaves the track standing 1.5mm proud of the baseboard surface allowing a neat ballast 'shoulder' to be created later. The cork also helps with sound deadening.

STEP 11

Repeating the process for the second line gives us a smart looking double track main line ready for the next phase of development.

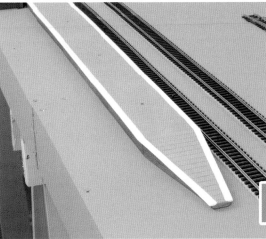

STEP 12

Part of the project calls for a bay platform to be added in the station. This means adding a curved section of track which the semi-flexible track is perfect for. First though, the platform needs to be positioned loosely to allow the bay platform track to be installed accurately.

STEP 13

Having checked the position of the platform, an express left-hand point (R8077) is joined to the main line and a yard length of semi-flexible track is joined to the point. As delivered this track is straight, but it can be shaped to suit specific locations.

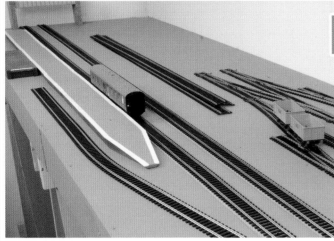

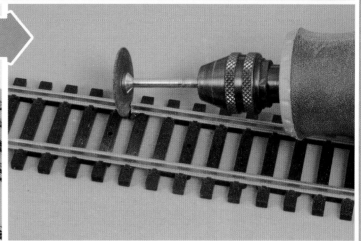

STEP 14

Having carefully shaped it, the track now neatly forms a curve into the bay platform at the front of the station. The track can now be placed onto cork with the excess being trimmed away as before.

STEP 15

The next skill involved in using semi-flexible or flexible track is cutting. There are two ways to do this – hand cutting using a junior hacksaw, which is the cheapest method, or using a compact multi-tool drill such as this Dremel. Fitted with a metal cutting disc, it makes light work of cutting through the track, but ensure your eyes are protected.

STEP 16

The final element to consider during track laying is the future control of points. If you plan on adding motorised points then now is the time to create the holes for them. Using a 1mm drill in a pin vice tiny pilot holes are made into the baseboard surface below.

STEP 17

The track is then lifted and a square of cork cut away to reveal the marks left by the 1mm drill. The pencil arrow helps locate the position of the 1mm holes.

STEP 18

Using a 5mm diameter drill bit, two holes are drilled in line across the width of the underside of the point tie bar and opened out to join into one long hole around 11mm long and 5mm wide. This allows space for a point motor actuating bar to move.

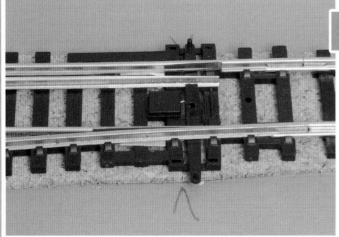

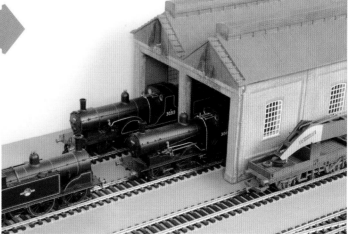

STEP 19

The point is then replaced in its original location and fixed in place. The holes are fully hidden by the point and an under baseboard mounting bracket (R8015) can be used to fit a point motor (R8014) under the point.

STEP 20

With track laying continuing using the same methods and styles the layout soon comes together ready for the start of scenic work. Read more about this station project on pages 106-111.

2016
TRAIN PACKS

Each year a new collection of train packs is released by Hornby. We preview this year's selection including commemorative packs.

The last steam hauled 'Golden Arrow' – R3400

Fifty five years ago the Southern Region of British Railways operated the last steam hauled 'Golden Arrow' Pullman from London Victoria to Dover Marine. The train, which operated on June 11 1961 in the hands of rebuilt Bulleid 'West Country' 4-6-2 34100 *Appledore*, is to be commemorated with a special train pack in 2016 featuring *Appledore* and a trio of eight-wheel Pullman cars with interior lighting. The Pullmans will be Kitchen First *Minerva* together with Parlour Second No. 34 and No. 36.

The pack will come with a full set of 'Golden Arrow' regalia for attaching to 34100 with the locomotive featuring BR lined green with late crests and a Stewarts Lane (73A) shecode on the smokebox door.

Rebuilt 'West Country' 4-6-2 34100 Appledore departs from London Victoria with the last steam hauled 'Golden Arrow' on Sunday June 11 1961. Brian Stephenson.

Intercity 125 40th anniversary – R3403

This year marks the 40th anniversary of the introduction of the Intercity High Speed Train (HST) for public service in 1976. The trains, which had a Class 43 power car at each end of a rake of new Mk 3 carriages, debuted on the Western Region of British Railways.

Hornby's train pack to mark the anniversary will feature a pair of power cars to represent set 253001 in original BR blue and grey with wrap around yellow warning panels. The power cars will be 43002 and 43003, which are ideal for representing mid-1970s and early 1980s HST operations on the Western Region.

2016 marks the 40th anniversary of the production HST sets entering service. On July 30 1983 set 253018 exits Whiteball Tunnel heading for Penzance. Railphotoprints.co.uk.

Lyme Regis branch line pack – R3398

The arrival of Hornby's Adams '0415' 4-4-2T is sure to spur interest in modelling the characterful six-mile long Lyme Regis branch along the Dorset-Devon border. Now closed, the route was home to three of these Victorian tank engines where their design suited the sharply curved and steeply graded route.

Making the most of the new models of the 'Radial tank' and Maunsell 58ft compartment stock, this new train pack allows a faithful reproduction of a Lyme Regis branch line train to be represented. The pack will contain '0415' 30583 in BR lined black with early crests while the carriages will be Maunsell ex-LSWR Brake Third S2636S and Brake Composite S6401S. ☞

The 'Queen of Scots' pack – R3402

Introduced by the London and North Eastern Railway in 1928, the 'Queen of Scots' Pullman ran from London King's Cross to Glasgow Queen Street via Leeds Central. The train launched the new all-steel K-Type Pullman carriages which were built for the train and this new train pack uses Hornby's new collection of models of this detailed carriages.

Heading up the pack is Gresley 'A4' 4-6-2 4500 *Garganey* in LNER garter blue, which will be accompanied by all-steel K-Type Brake Third No. 77, Kitchen First Thelma and Parlour First Sheila. Roofboards will be fitted to each carriage and a headboard for the 'A4' will be included as a separate fitting to complete the model.

EWS freight pack – R3399

EWS became the main freight operator in Britain in 1996 and continued its lead in the movement of goods by rail until its purchase by Deutsche Bahn in 2007. One of the prime locomotive introductions by EWS, alongside its well known Class 66, was the Alstom built fleet of 30 Class 67s. These 125mph Bo-Bo diesels were originally designed for parcels work, but have found wider use with the demise of this traffic on the railway.

New for 2016 is an EWS freight pack containing EWS Class 67 67003 in the company's maroon and gold colour scheme together with a trio of MHA wagons numbered 394652, 394653 and 394654. The wagons will be in matching EWS maroon and gold livery offering a simple means of starting a realistic privatisation freight train formation.

The 'Bristolian' 1935 – R3401

To celebrate the 100th anniversary of the Great Western Main Line to Bristol the Great Western Railway (GWR) introduced the 'Bristolian' named train in 1935 taking passengers non-stop from London Paddington to Bristol Temple Meads in 105 minutes. The train was formed of a GWR 'King' 4-6-0 and seven Collett bow-ended carriages. The 'Bristolian' name remained in use through British Railways operation and is still used today by Great Western Railway.

Hornby's new pack for the 'Bristolian' contains GWR 'King' 6009 *King Charles II* with 'shirtbutton' logos together with a trio of the new Collett bow-ended carriages. The carriages in the pack will be left-hand Brake Corridor Third 5108, right-hand Brake Corridor Third 5107 and left-hand Corridor Composite 6160. All three will be turned out in GWR chocolate and cream livery with 'Bristolian' roof boards fitted.

Virgin Trains East Coast 91107 *Skyfall* approaches Colton Junction on September 19 2015 carrying the train operators new livery. Andy Mason.

The 'Bristolian' is the subject of a new train pack for release in 2016. 'King' 4-6-0 6017 *King Edward IV* arrives at Paddington with an express in 1935. Lewis Coles/Rail Archive Stephenson.

Virgin Trains East Coast pack – R3501

The high profile East Coast Main Line franchise gained a new operator in March 2015 when the partnership of Virgin Trains and Stagecoach took over the route.

It operates trains north from London to Yorkshire, the North East and Scotland using fleets of Class 91 electric locomotives with Mk 4 carriages and Class 43 High Speed Train power cars with Mk 3 carriages. New for 2016 is a Virgin Train East Coast pack which will feature Class 91 91124, Mk 4 Driving Van Trailer 82219 and Mk 4 Tourist Open Seconds 12201 and 12401. All will be in Virgin Trains' new livery, representing one of the latest colour schemes on Britain's railway network.

LMS suburban passenger pack – R3397

Suburban trains were a huge part of daily operations on the railway system and this new train pack allows modellers to recreate a typical suburban working of the 1930s on the London Midland & Scottish Railway (LMS).

The pack contains Fowler '4P' 2-6-4T 2238 in LMS lined black together with a trio of Stanier 57ft non-corridor carriages. The vehicles are Brake Thirds 20768 and 20769 plus composite 16592 – all delivered in LMS lined maroon livery.

Fowler '4P' 2-6-4T 42312, still with LMS on its tank sides, approaches Heaton Lodge Junction with a Penistone-Mirfield-Bradford local in 1949-1950 formed of LMS liveried Stanier 57ft carriages. Kenneth Field/Rail Achive Stephenson.

BR's Class 71 electric locomotives

One of the more unusual fleets produced as a result of the modernisation of British Railways were the Class 71 electrics - a design built to satisfy the unique requirements of the railways of Southern England. Evan Green-Hughes explains the history of the Class 71 – a class which is soon to be released in model form.

When those in charge of our railways were considering how best to update and rebuild the system in the early years of the 1950s there was a great desire to re-equip with electric traction. This was seen as a suitable replacement for steam because the electricity required could be generated using the same coal that would otherwise have been burned in steam engines. This coal was, importantly, dug up at home and therefore did not involve precious currency having to be spent on imports, as would be required for oil should diesel traction be adopted.

With a pair of Southern Railway PMV vans providing luggage accommodation ahead of the Pullman cars, E5015 emerges from Saltwood Tunnel as it approaches Sandling with the Up 'Golden Arrow' in July 1960. *Railphotoprints.co.uk*

▼ With full 'Golden Arrow' boat train regalia fitted, Class 71 E5015 departs from London Victoria for Dover Marine on July 9 1961. The 'Golden Arrow' was a regular Class 71 duty from their introduction. *Brian Stephenson.*

> *In designing the Class 71, Doncaster made a study of continental practise where lightweight locomotives were very much in vogue.*

Class 71 E5022 nears completion in Doncaster paint shop on August 24 1960. *Brian Stephenson.*

Unfortunately the catch with this was the high initial cost of electrifying the whole network, something that was well out of the reach of a country crippled by its participation in two recent world wars. Therefore it was decided that only certain new routes would be wired up but amongst these were several in the Southern Region, an area that already had an extensive network of lines working on the third-rail DC system, and which had been steadily built up over the last half century or so.

Electrification south of the capital started in the early 1900s with the London and South Western Railway (LSWR) starting a 660v DC system in the suburbs of London. The London, Brighton and South Coast Railway and South Eastern and Chatham Railways also instigated third-rail electrification systems, but on the grouping of the railways in 1923 the Southern Railway adopted the LSWR principal, later increasing its voltage to 750v DC. The Southern Region third-rail network is now the largest of its kind in the world operating an intensive service of Electric Multiple Units (EMUs) from London into southern England.

The system developed in stages and one of the areas scheduled for development in the 1950s was the Kent coast and for this the third-rail was to be extended from Gillingham to Dover via Canterbury, and then along the coast to Ramsgate. As with other routes on the Southern Region it was envisaged that the majority of passenger traffic could be accommodated by using EMUs but there were two prestige services to the continent which would continue to use conventional coaches - the Pullman 'Golden Arrow' and the 'Night Ferry' which also included sleeping cars. For these duties and for a limited amount of goods traffic a small number of locomotives would be needed, with diesels being deemed to be unsuitable as there was a desire to operate an all-electric railway. ☞

N

Class 71 E5010 operates from the overhead wires at Grove Park in the 1960s. Colour Rail.

The '71s' were mixed traffic locomotives which were called upon for a wide range of duties from the 'Golden Arrow' Pullman train through to engineers' workings. In April 1959 E5003 waits to depart Brighton with an engineers' train. Railphotoprints.co.uk.

▲ While the carriage type used for the prestigious 'Golden Arrow' may have changed completely, the Class 71s were still regular motive power into the early 1970s. E5008 passes Orpington with the down 'Golden Arrow' from London Victoria to Dover March 28 1970. Railphotoprints.co.uk.

The Southern Region already possessed three electric locomotives that had been built for similar work dating from 1941 and these produced a useful 2,200hp but weighed 99tons, a considerable amount for a six-axle machine. These were solid and reliable engines and contained many features worth progressing but were too heavy and electrically primitive to be worth replicating as they were. Instead a new design was commissioned from Doncaster Works that was to incorporate the best features of the existing engines but include lightweight semi-integral bodywork and thus reduce the overall weight of the locomotives.

In designing what was to become the Class 71 Doncaster made a study of contemporary continental practice, where lightweight locomotives were very much in vogue. It was found possible to manufacture a locomotive with a slightly higher tractive effort than those existing while at the same time reducing overall weight by some 22tons. This enabled use of two four-wheel instead of two six-wheel bogies and meant a reduction in overall length was possible too. Each axle was powered but the traction motors were spring mounted, the first time that this feature had appeared on an electric locomotive in the UK. Power was transmitted using a Swiss-designed flexible drive system and the bogies themselves owed a great deal to European rather than UK practice.

One feature that was retained from the earlier engines was the incorporation of a 'booster' set. This was a piece of equipment that enabled the locomotive to continue to move for short distances using stored energy in the form of a flywheel and motor so that it did not get stuck where there were gaps in the third rail. Another idea from the earlier engines that was retained was the fitting of a pantograph in the centre of the roof and this was used to provide power when the locomotive was working in yards where the third-rail was not installed. Instead overhead wiring was provided of a type normally found on tramways but

which was sufficient for the low speed operation called for during shunting around yards.

Striking performance

The completed Class 71s weighed only 77 tons but could produce around 2,500hp giving a level of performance that had never before been previously available. It is said that when tackling the climb out of London Victoria – a formidable 1-in-62 - that they could be driven in a way that virtually ignored the gradient!

The fleet of 24 locomotives proved reliable right from the outset working the two express services for which they had been designed as well as finding employment on fitted freights, particularly those that brought perishables from the continent. Reliability was found to be first class and the locomotives established a very good reputation with traincrew and maintenance people alike.

However almost as soon as the new locomotives came on stream and were allocated to Stewart's Lane depot in London it became apparent that their design had a number of drawbacks. Due to the intense commuter nature of the Southern Region it was necessary to conduct any maintenance and repair work overnight, precisely at the time electric locomotives might be in use on freight trains and this meant that they often had to be replaced by diesels when diversions were in place or when power was interrupted.

The overhead wiring in goods yards also proved to ☞

▼ A pair of Class 71s headed by E5018 stand at Stewarts Lane Depot on March 7 1965. Initially the class was heavily used, but as work suitable for the all electric Bo-Bos reduced they spent more time stabled at their Stewarts Lane base. John Chalcraft/Railphotoprints. co.uk.

Class 71 E5012, now carrying BR blue livery, departs Dover yard with a fitted freight in June 1969. Railphotoprints.co.uk.

be expensive to maintain and of course not all yards were equipped with it. Consequently it was found that electric locomotives that had been fitted with small diesel engines were a better alternative when part of the duty involved working away from the main third rail system. Within a short period of time the idea of providing overhead wires in goods yards was done away with, further reducing the usefulness of the virtually new Class 71s.

As the 1960s progressed then so did the Southern's electrified track mileage, with one of the biggest schemes being the extension of the third-rail to Southampton and Bournemouth.

As this came close to completion it caused the Region's management to undertake a review of their locomotive requirements.

As with previous schemes there remained the need for some conventional trains on the newly-upgraded section but this time a specification was drawn up for a more powerful locomotive that would be able to work passenger trains at 90mph on the same timings as the multiple units. Taking into account previous experience it was also deemed necessary to include the facility for working off electrified lines on diesel power whenever required. By this time it had been decided that all future electric locomotives would be to

this specification and what resulted was a design which eventually became known as the Class 73.

New ideas

It was soon noted that the new Class 73 electro-diesels, though not as powerful as the Class 71s, seemed able to undertake all the duties of the older class, with the added advantage that they could

operate in whatever yard or siding was required without the necessity for overhead wires or the third rail. By this time the Class 71s had only limited passenger work and were being used on newspaper trains from Victoria to the coast at Dover and Ramsgate but even then it was becoming increasingly difficult to keep them all employed due to a lack of suitable duties.

With there being a shortage of electro-diesels and a surplus of straight electric locomotives it is perhaps no surprise that an investigation took place to see whether a conversion of the Class 71 was a possibility.

Ten of the class had already been stood down from regular service and these were shipped off to Crewe works where they were rebuilt. A 650hp Paxman six-cylinder engine was fitted and this was wired into the old booster unit while unnecessary features such as the pantograph were removed. Buckeye couplers were fitted as were high-level control air and brake pipes. After conversion into Class 74 electro-diesels these locomotives were envisaged as suitable for working boat trains to Southampton and Bournemouth which included short stretches of working onto the non-electrified quaysides.

The locomotives selected for rebuilding were taken at random from the Class 71 fleet and as a result the remaining engines were renumbered to fill in the gaps

E5016 shows its Bo-Bo design at Stewarts Lane depot in April 1962. A. Baldwyn/Rail Archive Stephenson.

E5015 arrives at London Victoria with the 'Golden Arrow' Pullman train for Dover in September 1962. *Lewis Coles/Rail Archive Stephenson.*

left by the conversions, which were renumbered in the E6100 series. This was the second time that some engines had been renumbered, giving rise to a great deal of confusion as to the identity of individual machines.

The Class 74s had regular work from Waterloo to Weymouth but were displaced from this by further builds of EMUs and consequently were soon cascaded on to freight and parcels work. The conversions spent their entire careers based at Eastleigh.

Although the overall numbers of Class 71s had been reduced to just 14 locomotives the class was still under-employed due to its restricted availability and it is therefore not surprising that when the Southern Region conducted another motive power survey in 1977 it was concluded that the class could be dispensed with and that their remaining duties could be adequately covered by diesels such as the Class 33 and by the Class 73 electro-diesels. At this point none of the '71s' had been withdrawn although two were in works at the time the decision was taken to withdrawn them. As a result the remaining 14 that had not been converted to Class 74s were all withdrawn despite still being in full working order.

Class 74 problems

By this time one of the conversions, 74006 (E6106) had already been taken out of service following a fire and there were serious issues with the electronic control systems fitted to the rest. Traditional locomotive work, such as the boat trains, was declining as was freight leading to a surplus of motive power and so the seven remaining conversions followed their Class 71 cousins to the scrapyard at the end of 1977. The two others had already been taken out of service during the year, one following a collision and the other following a failure in service. There was hope that one might survive when 74010 was taken to Derby for potential Research Department use but the locomotive never worked in this guise and was despatched for cutting up two years later.

Fortunately one of the original examples was claimed for the National Collection and was despatched to York shortly after withdrawal. E5001, which had latterly been 71001, was restored to its original livery and condition. After preservation it appeared on the main line and worked a number of specials in the 1990s, also visiting some works open days and other special events. The locomotive spent a long time on display at York

BR CLASS 71 NUMBERING

As built	1957	Class 74	TOPS
E5000	E5024	E6104	74004
E5001	E5001		71001
E5002	E5002		71002
E5003		E6107	74007
E5004	E5004		71004
E5005		E6108	74008
E5006		E6103	74003
E5007	E5007		71007
E5008	E5008		71008
E5009	E5009		71009
E5010	E5010		71010
E5011	E5011		71011
E5012	E5012		71012
E5013	E5013		71013
E5014	E5014		71014
E5015	E5015	E6101	74001
E5016	E5016	E6102	74002
E5017	E5017	E6109	74009
E5018	E5003		71003
E5019		E6105	74005
E5020	E5005		71005
E5021		E6110	74010
E5022	E5006		71006
E5023		E6106	74006

and later at Locomotion in Shildon but in recent years has been out on loan at Barrow Hill.

Obsolete

The Class 71s were built to answer a specific need for a locomotive to work what were basically steam era style trains on a network that was modernising very quickly. Consequently they became obsolete as the trains for which they were built either ceased to run or were handed over to multiple units.

That they existed for only 20 years in main line service is not a testament to poor design, for they were very well built and had many years' life left in them when they were withdrawn, but rather that they were no longer suited for the work on offer. They were, however, a complete success in engineering terms and, although overlooked in favour of more glamorous motive power for many years, are now gaining some of the attention that they rightly deserve. Ⓗ

Connecting power

Every model railway needs to be connected to a controller to power the trains. Mike Wild shows how to make neat soldered wiring connections.

Hornby's train sets are all supplied with a power connecting track which makes it a superbly simple and quick process to connect a controller to the track.

The power track is a great invention, but when it comes to creating a scenic model railway you might want to turn to a method which is less obtrusive. There are a number of ways to do this. You could use pre-wired rail joiners which are available from third party companies or hide the power connecting track within the scenery or out of sight.

One method which has stood the test of time is using a soldering iron to connect wires to the side of the rails. Many find the thought

of using a soldering iron daunting, but it needn't be. Good quality soldering irons are surprisingly cheap to buy. A standard 25w Antex iron, as used here, will cost around £20. They are supplied pre-fitted with a mains plug and a stand can be bought to support them while not in use. Using one is simple too – Antex's product is such that it provides heat effectively to create strong joints between wires using the right type of electrical solder.

There are other tools you will need too. A pair of wire strippers is essential for removing the insulation from equipment wire –

never be tempted to use a craft knife for this as it could damage the wire, or worse, slip and damage your hands - while a pair of side cutters and a small blade screwdriver are the only other essential tools for the job.

When it comes to wire there are a few things to bear in mind. Firstly, pick at least two colours – one for the left rail, one for the right. We recommend red and black as these are easily distinguished from one another. Also, always use multi-core wire for model railway applications. This is wire formed of a number of fine strands of copper wire which are much more flexible

and robust than single core wires and therefore less likely to break through bending. We use 7/0.2 equipment – that's seven strands of copper wire each 0.2mm thick inside the insulation sleeve.

One final component that we regularly use in model railway wiring is plug-in terminal blocks. These are an ideal means of connecting sections together or connecting the wires from the rails to a controller. They have screw terminals which makes them simple to work with and making changes is as simple as undoing a screw and swapping a wire. They come in strips of 12 with male and female elements to allow them to be pushed together to create a reliable electrical joint.

The step by step guide explains how we go about adding power connections to the side of rails.

TOOLS

- 25watt soldering iron
- Wire stripper
- Side cutters
- Electric drill
- 2mm drill bit
- Small flat blade screwdriver

Connecting power to the track using soldered connections can disguise wiring altogether leading to a more realistic model railway.

STEP **BY** STEP ADDING POWER CONNECTIONS

STEP 1
Hornby's power track is a very simple means of connecting power to the track – and it works superbly. However, if you are creating a scenic layout it can look out of place unless it is carefully disguised. The alternative is to solder wires to the track, as we'll show here.

STEP 2
A handful of tools are essential for making neat connections to the track with soldering. Here we have a 25w soldering iron, wire strippers, side cutters, 7/0.2 equipment wire in red and black, a plug-in terminal block, a small flat blade screwdriver and a reel of electrical solder.

STEP 3
To hide the connecting wires we need to send them through the baseboard to be connected underneath. Using an electric drill, a 2mm diameter hole is made on each side of the track where a wire is to be connected.

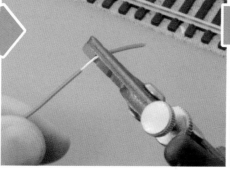

STEP 4
Next, the insulation is stripped off the end of a length of equipment wire using wire strippers – don't be tempted to use alternative tools as they will damage either the wire or you! We strip around 20mm of insulation from the wire.

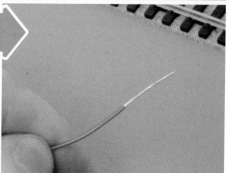

STEP 5
The bare wire will now be a collection of strands with insulation removed. Twist them together with your fingers to create a single flexible length of bare wire.

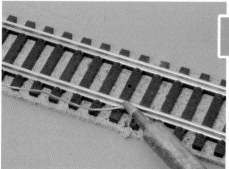

STEP 6
Allow the soldering iron to heat up fully before starting this stage – a part heated iron will not heat the rails or the solder correctly. Heat a small amount of solder onto the rail side, pressing the iron against the rail for no more than a few seconds to avoid heat transfer into the plastic sleepers.

STEP 7
You will now have a small spot of solder on the side of the rail like this positioned just above the hole for the wire.

STEP 8
Tin the end of the bare wire you wish to solder to the rail by heating a small amount of solder on to it and then hold it in position against the previously applied spot of solder on the rail side and heat the two elements. Keep the wire perfectly still after removing the soldering iron for a reliable joint.

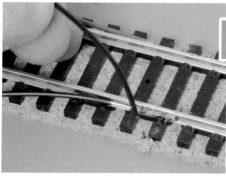

STEP 9
The wire can now feed through the hole in the baseboard. Repeat this for each wiring connection so that the wires disappear out of sight below the baseboard surface.

STEP 10
Once completed your wires should look like this. The small amount of black insulation showing here will be hidden by ballasting of the track in the next phase of the project.

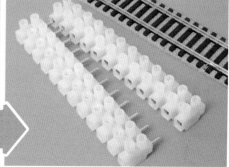

STEP 11
To connect the wires from the rails back to the controller we used plug-in terminal blocks. These are supplied in strips of 12 which push together.

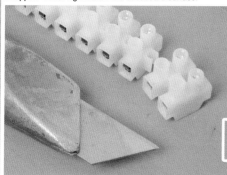

STEP 12
Cutting off a pair of connections from the strip with a craft knife prepares us for the next step – connecting the wires to the controller.

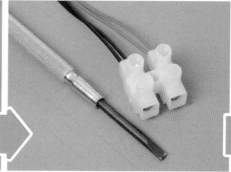

STEP 13
We had two pairs of wires for this Digital Command Control (DCC) layout to take back to the controller. Both were connected into the same terminal block.

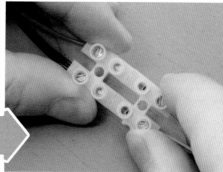

STEP 14
By adding a plug to wires coming from the controller (green and orange) the wires from the track (black and red) can be easily connected to the power source.

Collett and Maunsell lead 2016
CARRIAGE RANGE

With a stunning collection of more than 80 new carriages planned for 2016, we take a closer look at what is in store from in this exciting line up.

Two new rakes of carriages are leading Hornby's line up of passenger rolling stock in 2016 covering the Collett bow-ended corridor stock and the Maunsell 58ft compartment stock rebuilt from LSWR 48ft vehicles. These will be joined by an extensive list of new vehicles based on the existing range of products.

The Collett carriages are only Hornby's second foray into top of the range Great Western Railway designs. They follow on from the 2010 released Hawkworth vehicles, but these bow-ended carriages have a totally different feel.

They were introduced in 1925 and featured distinctively short 7ft bogies. The bow-ends reduced the length of the corridor connections between vehicles, improving the ride for passengers when moving from one coach to another. The bow-ended stock was built in left and right-hand corridor formats to allow a complete train to arrive at the station with the corridors of all vehicles facing the platforms. This was very different from other railways using side corridor stock where the corridor position could vary between vehicles marshalled next to each other in the train.

Hornby's range of vehicles covers five designs – the right-hand Brake Third and Corridor Composite together with a left-hand Brake Third, Composite and Third. Each vehicle will feature turned metal wheels and small tension lock couplings in NEM pockets. Detailing includes brackets for roof boards together with correct roof vent and rivet detail and changes to the window arrangement to suit each vehicle type.

On release the new Collett carriages will be released in 1930s GWR chocolate and cream livery across all five vehicles together with a set in 1950s BR carmine and cream also planned into the 2016 range.

Maunsell rebuilds

Hornby garnered a high reputation for quality carriages with its extensive range of Southern Railway Maunsell corridor stock. New for 2016 is a collection of vehicles representing those rebuilt from London & South Western Railway (LSWR) 48ft bogie stock into 58ft stock by Maunsell.

Rebuilding of the 48ft stock started in 1934 and saw the vehicles turned out on new standard 58ft underframes with extended bodies. Gas lighting was upgraded to electric lighting and the vehicles were formed mainly into two car sets. They were best known for operation on the Lyme Regis branch with the Adams 'Radial' 4-4-2Ts. Service also took them to other routes in the South West including the Okehampton, Sidmouth and Torrington branches while some ended up as individual vehicles which were worked in other formations. ☞

Hornby's new set of Collett bow-ended carriages offers an impressive range of five vehicles covering brake, composite and third class vehicles in both left and right hand corridor formats.

The Collett bow-ended carriages were introduced in 1925 and were put to work on prestigious named trains. In October 1935 GWR 'King' 4-6-0 6018 *King Henry VI* stands at Exeter St Davids with a rake of matching bow-ended vehicles. Hornby's 2016 range includes a set of five different Collett vehicles with their distinctive 7ft bogies. Colour Rail.

The Maunsell 58ft rebuilds were more commonly found working in two-car sets, but in the BR era they could be found working separately too. On September 10 1950 Drummond 'M7' 0-4-4T 30047 departs Rogate with the Petersfield-Midhurst branch train formed of a single eight compartment Brake Second. E.C. Griffith/Rail Archive Stephenson.

Hornby's models will cover four vehicle types which will initially be released in Southern Railway and British Railways green liveries. The vehicle types in production are the eight compartment Brake Third, six compartment Brake Composite Lavatory, six compartment Brake Third Lavatory and nine compartment Third Lavatory.

Reintroductions

The range of carriage designs available to Hornby is extensive and the New Year promises an impressive range of new vehicles to either increase existing formations or to go with specific releases in the locomotive section.

Highlights include a new set of Maunsell corridor stock in Southern Railway malachite green, new sets of Stanier 57ft stock in LMS lined maroon and BR maroon plus a set of Gresley corridor stock in BR carmine and cream.

TABLE 1 – NEW CARRIAGES 2016

Vehicle	Description	Period	Cat No.
GWR Collett Corridor Third	4548, GWR chocolate and cream	1930s	R4679
GWR Collett Corridor Brake Third (RH)	5131, GWR chocolate and cream	1930s	R4680
GWR Collett Corridor Brake Third (LH)	5132, GWR chocolate and cream	1930s	R4681
GWR Collett Corridor Composite (LH)	6520, GWR chocolate and cream	1930s	R4682
GWR Collett Corridor Composite (RH)	TBA , GWR chocolate and cream	1930s	R4683
GWR Collett Corridor Third	W4857W, BR carmine and cream	1950s	R4684
GWR Collett Corridor Brake Third (RH)	W5091W, BR carmine and cream	1950s	R4685
GWR Collett Corridor Brake Third (LH)	W5092W, BR carmine and cream	1950s	R4686
GWR Collett Corridor Composite (LH)	W6030W, BR carmine and cream	1950s	R4687
GWR Collett Corridor Composite (RH)	W6029W, BR carmine and cream	1950s	R4688
SR 58ft eight comp' Brake Third	2639, SR olive green (set 45)	1930s	R4717
SR 58ft six comp' Composite	2626, SR olive green	1930s	R4718
SR 58ft six comp' Third	6404, SR olive green (set 45)	1930s	R4719
SR 58ft nine comp' Third	304, SR olive green	1930s	R4720
SR 58ft eight comp' Brake Second	S2637S, BR Southern Region green (set 43)	1950s	R4746
SR 58ft six comp' Composite	S2629S, BR Southern Region green	1950s	R4747
SR 58ft six comp' Second	S6402S, BR Southern Region green	1950s	R4748
SR 58ft nine comp' Second	S267S, BR Southern Region green (set 43)	1950s	R4749
SR Maunsell Corridor First	7406, Southern Railway malachite	1940s	R4734
SR Maunsell Corridor Third	1216, Southern Railway malachite	1940s	R4735
SR Maunsell Brake Third	3797, Southern Railway malachite (six compartment)	1940s	R4736
SR Maunsell Brake Third	3798, Southern Railway malachite (six compartment)	1940s	R4737
BR Maunsell push-pull pack	Set 619, BR Southern Region green	1960s	R4534D
SR '2-SET W' coach pack	Set 109, BR Southern Region green (BCK, SO)	1950s/1960s	R4745
LMS 57ft non-corridor Composite	16612, LMS lined maroon	1930s/1940s	R4656A
LMS 57ft non-corridor Third	11718, LMS lined maroon	1930s/1940s	R4657A
LMS 57ft non-corridor Brake Third	20754, LMS lined maroon	1930s/1940s	R4677B
LMS 57ft non-corridor Brake Third	20755, LMS lined maroon	1930s/1940s	R4677C
LMS 57ft non-corridor Composite	M16574M, BR maroon	1950s	R4689
LMS 57ft non-corridor Third	M11912M, BR maroon	1950s	R4690
LMS 57ft non-corridor Brake Third	M20787M, BR maroon	1950s	R4691
LMS 57ft non-corridor Brake Third	M20788M, BR maroon	1950s	R4691A
LMS Corridor First	M1080M, BR maroon	1950s/1960s	R4234B
LMS Corridor Second	M1741M, BR maroon	1950s/1960s	R4235C
LMS Corridor Brake Second	M5806M, BR maroon	1950s/1960s	R4236C
LMS 68ft dining car	M232M, BR maroon	1950s/1960s	R4131C
LNER Gresley Corridor Buffet	E9114E, BR carmine and cream	1950s	R4181B
LNER Gresley Corridor composite	E10106E, BR carmine and cream	1950s	R4178C
LNER Gresley Corridor Second	E12549E, BR carmine and cream	1950s	R4180B
LNER Gresley Corridor First	E11003E, BR carmine and cream	1950s	R4179B
LNER Gresley Composite	32480, LNER varnished teak	1930s/1940s	R4517B
LNER Gresley Brake Third	3738, LNER varnished teak	1930s/1940s	R4518B
LNER Gresley Third	21022, LNER varnished teak	1930s/1940s	R4516B

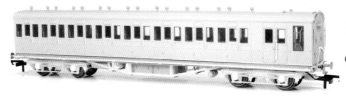

The new set of Maunsell 58ft stock comprises an eight-compartment Brake Third, a six compartment Brake Composite Lavatory, a six compartment Brake Second Lavatory

The popular new range of BR Mk 1 carriages is also in for fresh running numbers with Western Region chocolate and cream, Southern Region green and BR carmine and cream and maroon vehicles due out in 2016.

This will use the Brake Second Corridor, Corridor Composite and Second Open models as well as Full Brakes and a Tourist Second Open. 10 new Pullmans are also on the list with five using the new all-steel K-Type vehicles

introduced in 2015.

For modern modellers a new set of Mk 2e stock using the late 2014 introduced models is planned in Virgin Trains livery while the Mk 3 carriages will be released in BR blue and grey and Virgin Trains

East Coast liveries to go with new HST power car packs for release in 2016.

See Table 1 for the full list of new carriages for 2016 and visit *www.hornby.com* for further information. Ⓗ

Vehicle	Description	Period	Cat No.
LNER Thompson Composite	88426, LNER varnished teak	1940s	R4572A
LNER Thompson Third	82646, LNER varnished teak	1940s	R4573A
LNER Thompson Brake Third	87019, LNER varnished teak	1940s	R4574A
Pullman Parlour First	*Lydia*, Pullman umber and cream	1950s	R4738
Pullman Parlour Third	Car No. 34, Pullman umber and cream	1950s	R4739
Pullman Kitchen First	*Argus*, Pullman umber and cream	1950s	R4740
Pullman Kitchen Third	Car No. 58, Pullman umber and cream	1950s	R4741
Pullman Brake Third	Car No. 162, Pullman umber and cream	1950s	R4742
All-steel K-Type Pullman Kitchen Third	Car No. 67, Pullman umber and cream, grey roof	1950s	R4693
All-steel K-Type Pullman Parlour Third	Car No. 83, Pullman umber and cream, grey roof	1950s	R4694
All-steel K-Type Pullman Brake Third	Car No. 80, Pullman umber and cream, grey roof	1950s	R4695
All-steel K-Type Pullman Kitchen First	*Joan*, Pullman umber and cream, grey roof	1950s	R4696
All-steel K-Type Pullman Parlour First	*Ursula*, Pullman umber and cream, grey roof	1950s	R4697
BR Mk 1 Full Brake	E80534, BR carmine and cream	1950s	R4698
BR Mk 1 Full Brake	S80926, BR Southern Region green	1950s/1960s	R4699
BR Mk 1 Second Open	M4487, BR maroon	1950s/1960s	R4700
BR Mk 1 Tourist Second Open	M3947, BR maroon	1950s/1960s	R4701
BR Mk 1 Corridor Second	E24162, BR carmine and cream	1950s	R4705
BR Mk 1 Corridor Composite	E15058, BR carmine and cream	1950s	R4706
BR Mk 1 Corridor Brake Second	E34010, BR carmine and cream	1950s	R4707
BR Mk 1 Corridor Second	W24540, BR chocolate and cream	1950s/1960s	R4708
BR Mk 1 Corridor Composite	W15061, BR chocolate and cream	1950s/1960s	R4709
BR Mk 1 Corridor Brake Second	W34290, BR chocolate and cream	1950s/1960s	R4710
BR MK 1 Corridor Second	S24316, BR Southern Region green	1950s/1960s	R4711
BR Mk 1 Corridor Composite	S15913, BR Southern Region green	1950s/1960s	R4712
BR Mk 1 Corridor Brake Second	S34613, BR Southern Region green	1950s/1960s	R4713
BR Mk 1 Corridor Second	M24912, BR maroon	1950s/1960s	R4714
BR Mk 1 Corridor Composite	M15679, BR maroon	1950s/1960s	R4715
BR Mk 1 Corridor Composite	M34672, BR maroon	1950s/1960s	R4716
BR Mk 2E Standard Open	5801, Virgin Trains	1990s/2000s	R4702
BR Mk 2E Standard Open	5787, Virgin Trains	1990s/2000s	R4702A
BR Mk 2E Brake Standard Open	9507, Virgin Trains	1990s/2000s	R4704
BR Mk 3 Buffet	40001, BR Intercity blue and grey	1970/1980s	R4729
BR Mk 3 First Open	41003, BR Intercity blue and grey	1970/1980s	R4730
BR Mk 3 First Open	41004, BR Intercity blue and grey	1970/1980s	R4730A
BR Mk 3 Tourist Second Open	42003, BR Intercity blue and grey	1970/1980s	R4732
BR Mk 3 Tourist Second Open	42004, BR Intercity blue and grey	1970/1980s	R4732A
BR Mk 3 Trailer Guard Standard	44050, Virgin Trains East Coast	2015-2016	R4750
BR Mk 3 Tourist Second Open	42322, Virgin Trains East Coast	2015-2016	R4751
BR Mk 3 Tourist Second Open	42130, Virgin Trains East Coast	2015-2016	R4751A
BR Mk 3 First Open	41159, Virgin Trains East Coast	2015-2016	R4752
BR Mk 3 Buffet	40708, Virgin Trains East Coast	2015-2016	R4753

and a nine compartment Second Lavatory. Each vehicle will be released in Southern Railway olive green and BR Southern Region green liveries.

Decoder fitting

R8249 – STANDARD 8-PIN DECODER

This standard 8-pin DCC decoder comes factory fitted with a harness to allow the decoder to be plugged directly into any model with an 8-pin socket where there is space to fit it. Measuring 17mm x 10mm x 3.5mm this is a relatively small chip and it is useful for fitting in steam locomotives when the decoder socket is located in the boiler and space is at premium, but it is equally useable for diesel locomotives. It can control four functions and has a continuous rating of 0.5amps.

R8245 – SAPPHIRE 21PIN/8-PIN DECODER

The Sapphire is Hornby's top of the range decoder and it is versatile in that it features a 21-pin connection and an adapter to convert it to connect to 8-pin decoder sockets. The decoder itself is bigger than the standard R8249 decoder – it measures 23mm x 17mm x 5mm – but it also has more features including fuel simulation, automatic control and low speed gearing for shunting operation as well as a 1amp continuous rating. It can operate four functions with 200mA available for each. It is suited to all types of locomotive where there is space to install it.

X9659 – 4-PIN MICRO DECODER

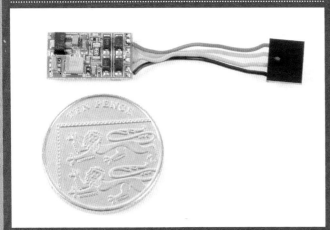

This decoder has been created specifically to suit Hornby's smallest locomotives as well as a handful of its trainset engines. It was launched to suit the 2014 released Sentinel 4wDH/0-4-0 shunter and it will also be used by the new Peckett 0-4-0ST for 2016. It has the same functions as the R8249 decoder and features a compact 4-pin socket as the locomotives it controls only feature motor and pick up wiring. It measures just 17mm x 10mm x 3.5mm but due to its four wire connection it cannot control any additional functions beyond the motor.

Enhancing the operating potential of a digital model railway means installing decoders. Mike Wild explains their purpose and shows how to install them in the latest generation of steam and diesel locomotives by Hornby.

Digital Command Control (DCC) is a big part of the model railway sector and a growing element within the UK market. Its popularity has come about through the increased abilities to control a model locomotive, further mimicking real life, as well as the option to bring in features such as sound.

Building a DCC model railway means installing decoders in locomotives. The decoder is an essential component which interprets signals sent by a DCC controller to control the speed of the motor, turn on lights and more. The difference between DCC and conventional analogue control is that DCC sends control signals to a specific locomotive, while analogue simply increases the current to the track, affecting every locomotive on a given section. Almost all of the Hornby range now comes factory fitted with a decoder socket to allow simple fitting of a DCC chip – exceptions include the Hunslet 'Austerity' 0-6-0ST and 'Terrier' 0-6-0T – with all but the Sentinel 4wDH shunter featuring a standard 8-pin socket. This socket is one of three standards used across the model railway market with the others being a 6-pin socket for compact locomotives and a 21-pin socket which offers greater function control. A fourth decoder type is produced by Hornby – the 4-pin decoder to suit its diminutive Sentinel diesel shunter.

In total there are three DCC decoders in the Hornby range. Its four function decoder (Cat No. R8249) is its smallest while at the top of the range is its Sapphire decoder (R8245) which is a 21-pin decoder supplied with a 21-pin to 8-pin harness to make it universal between the two most common formats of decoder socket. Hornby's two main decoders can be used in any locomotive from any manufacturer as they are fully compliant with the standard for digital control.

The actual installation of a decoder will vary from locomotive to locomotive in small details. All will follow the same basic process, but due to the nature of models the interior spaces available are different in each design as are the position of body securing screws.

In steam locomotives there are two different positions where you will find a decoder socket – in the boiler or in the tender. In recent years Hornby has moved towards tender mounting all decoder sockets for its main range, but some – including the recent Crosti '9F' 2-10-0 and the 2014 released Gresley 'P2' 2-8-2 and BR '8P' 4-6-2 – feature a boiler mounted decoder socket for the DCC ready versions. Tender decoder sockets are simpler to access and more space is available too.

Diesel locomotives have the decoder socket positioned on top of the chassis on the main printed circuit board (PCB) and space is usually provided at the No. 2 end of a diesel – the opposite end to the roof fan grille – to accommodate the decoder.

With practice installing standard motor control decoders is a straightforward and quick process which will take a matter of minutes to complete. The guides with this feature show how to install a decoder in a steam and diesel locomotive using the Hornby Gresley 'A3' 4-6-2 and BR Class 56 diesel as the subjects.

STEP 1

The design and position of fittings varies from locomotive to locomotive and individual manuals explain how to remove tender bodies for access. This is Hornby's Gresley 'A3' 4-6-2 with an eight-wheel tender – the tools required for the job are a set of jeweller's crosshead and flat blade screwdrivers together with a roll of electrical tape.

STEP 2

It is important to secure the model prior to working on it. A simple way of ensuring the model is held firmly is to use its plastic packaging inverted to allow access to the screw underneath the tender.

STEP 3

A single crosshead screw secures the tender body to its chassis. It is located underneath the coupling at the rear of the tender. To remove the coupling gently prize the fish tail socket out of its housing with upwards pressure from a small flat blade jeweller's screwdriver.

STEP 4

With the coupling removed a crosshead screwdriver can be lowered into the access hole to reach the screw head. Unwind the screw until it is fully released.

STEP 5

Turning the model over back on its wheels the tender body can now be removed by lifting it up from the rear to disengage the clip at the front.

STEP 6

With the body removed we can see how much space is available. The 'A3' with its full height Gresley eight-wheel tender is a simple installation as there is ample space inside for a decoder to be fitted. It is important to ensure that any bare metal faces are covered with electrical tape to stop any chance of a short circuit occurring – electrical shorts kill decoders!

Gearbox

Motor

Four-wire harness

8-pin decoder socket

Tender pick ups

STEP **BY** STEP HOW TO INSTALL A SAPPHIRE DECODER IN A **STEAM LOCOMOTIVE**

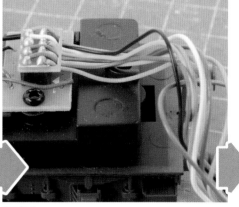

STEP 7
The 8-pin socket is mounted towards the rear of the tender. This model also has a cast metal weight on the tender chassis with space underneath for the fitting of a speaker for digital sound. All decoder sockets are configured in the same pattern and it is important to find and note the position of pin 1 as this locates the decoder plug correctly.

STEP 8
Removing the blanking plug is a simple step. Using gentle pressure pull the blanking plug upwards vertically – don't twist it on the way out as it could damage the pins on the blank or the socket.

STEP 9
The plug on the decoder can now be connected to the socket. Pin 1 is always noted by the position of the orange wire on a wired decoder harness plug. Position this correctly on the decoder and press it gently into place.

STEP **BY** STEP HOW TO INSTALL A SAPPHIRE DECODER IN A **DIESEL LOCOMOTIVE**

STEP 1
Diesel locomotives can be very straightforward to fit with a decoder, but the position needs to be considered carefully to ensure that the body fits back onto the chassis properly. The subject for this installation is a BR Class 56.

STEP 2
To ensure the model is held securely while being worked on the plastic tray from its box was used to support the inverted model. Four screws hold the body to the chassis and they are located above the bogies. Turning the bogies to the sides reveals the position of the screws which can be released with a flat blade screwdriver.

STEP 3
With the four screws released the body of the Class 56 simply slides up off the chassis vertically. The position of screws varies between locomotives while some have a simple clip on bodyshell.

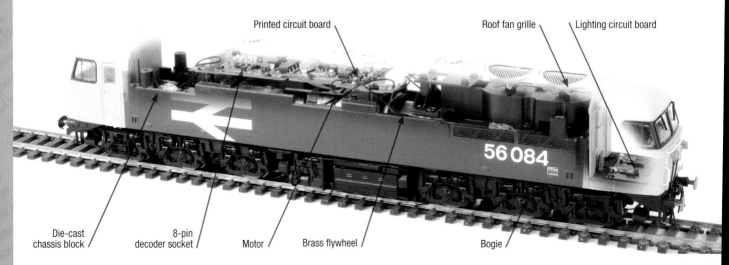

Printed circuit board

Roof fan grille

Lighting circuit board

Die-cast chassis block

8-pin decoder socket

Motor

Brass flywheel

Bogie

STEP 10
The decoder is now fitted and ready to install. It needs to be positioned neatly on top of the cast metal weight, but placing a decoder with exposed electrical surfaces on a metal weight isn't the way forward…

STEP 11
To ensure the decoder is safe from any potential electrical shorts a short length of rubber sleeve is placed over the decoder. The open ends will allow heat to dissipate while the sleeve keeps the decoder away from any contact with exposed metal. Note that the wires have been curved on top of the socket to keep them neat.

STEP 12
To complete the installation, the tender body is refitted in a reversal of dismantling. With the decoder neatly positioned inside there is no external sign of its installation.

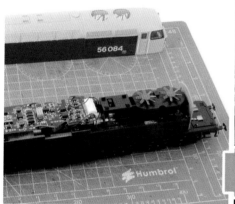

STEP 4
Removal of the body reveals the model's internal workings. The decoder socket is the small green printed circuit board located to the right of the main circuit board. The position of the circuit board means the decoder needs to be positioned carefully.

STEP 5
Removal of the decoder blank is carried out in the same way as with the steam locomotive. A pair of angled tweezers is helpful in removing sockets from compact spaces.

STEP 6
Fitting the Sapphire decoder – having correctly established the position of pin 1 on both the socket and the decoder plug – is simple and requires a single kink to be formed in the harness to keep its installation neat. The decoder sits comfortably against the cab bulkhead.

STEP 7
Refitting the body and tightening the screws from underneath completes this simple installation for the Class 56 in a matter of minutes.

How to make a
Tunnel

Building a tunnel for a model railway is a useful and appealing project. Ian Goodman explains the basics of forming your own model railway landscape.

A Class 60 waits in the siding as a Class 56 passes on the main line with a coal train. The tunnel portal makes an ideal end to a scenic section.

Tunnels are a great feature for a model railway. They are simple to add and can create the illusion of a train going forward on its journey and appearing somewhere else. In exhibition layouts tunnels are often used to create an end to a scenic section, making them a very useful visual feature.

There are several methods when it comes to creating tunnels and all have their own merits. The style we are going to show here is quick and simple to construct. It revolves around blocks of polystyrene insulation or packing material glued together to create height around the railway and above the tunnel entrance. The entrance in this case is the Skaledale double track brick tunnel portal (Cat No. R8512). We used a curved piece of black card to create a clean but dark environment inside the tunnel.

Building up model railway scenery is all about working in layers. Each one overlaps the previous layer, blending it in to the overall landscape. Once the landscape has been created with polystyrene and carved to shape with a double sided handsaw it is covered with plaster bandage which creates a solid land form onto which ground cover textures can be applied.

Like the process of making the land form, ground cover is best approached in layers. First, a base colour of brown or grey is painted over the entire area to be treated. Once this is dry a first layer of ground cover turf from the Skale Scenics range is applied using neat PVA wood glue to hold it in place. After allowing time for that to dry, the next layers on this project are a combination of fine turfs and a really useful product called static grass, available from model shops, which is fine fibres which when applied to a layout with a static charge from a suitable puffer bottle or applicator stand on end to better represent grasses in the real world.

The finishing touches are a collection of readily available foliage, fine and coarse turfs and coloured turfs available from model shops. The completed model represents the approaches to a tunnel with the structure of the tunnel portal fully bedded into the scene. ☛

TOOLS

- Handsaw
- Scissors
- Paintbrushes
- PVA glue
- Contact adhesive

STEP 1
The starting point of this project was to lay semi-flexible track on a cork base as shown on pages 38-43 and then to mock up the position of the tunnel portal (Cat No. R8512). This was adjusted and moved several times before the final position was decided.

STEP 2
The track was weathered with Humbrol No. 29 and the tunnel mouth was glued in place using contact adhesive and left to set in place. The addition of side walls (Cat No. R8545) supports the main tunnel portal, which has been set at an angle across the tracks for visual impact.

STEP **BY** STEP   BUILDING A TUNNEL WITH POLYSTYRENE

STEP 3

To give the tunnel a dark interior and to keep it looking 'clean' inside, a piece of A4 sized black card was cut to suit the angle of the tunnel portal and rolled to form the tunnel interior. If you wanted to go further with detail this could be lined with brick paper.

STEP 4

Using blocks of polystyrene insulation from a DIY store – you could use polystyrene packaging to keep the costs down – a basic landform is built up around and over the tunnel. The blocks are bonded together with 'no more nails' type adhesive and allowed to set in place.

STEP 5

The next stage is a messy process with polystyrene and it needs to be treated with care too. We use a double sided handsaw to carve the polystyrene blocks to shape. This makes quick work of the blocks, but the resulting mess takes some cleaning up!

STEP 6

With the blocks carved roughly to shape the amount of debris created is clear to see…

STEP 7

… but cleaning away all the debris reveals the new shape that we have carved out of the polystyrene blocks. It now needs covering with plaster cloth to give it a solid cover layer onto which ground cover textures can be applied.

STEP 8

Plaster cloth – readily available from model shops and supplied in rolls about 6in wide – is cut into strips using scissors to create sections measuring no more than 6in x 6in. Each piece is then dipped in water and laid onto the polystyrene landform, building up multiple layers. This then needs to be left to dry overnight. Remember to cover the track with newspaper during this process to protect it.

STEP 9

The white colour of plaster cloth isn't ideal as the base colour for ground cover. The final preparation before applying ground cover textures is to paint it all either brown or grey using water based paints.

STEP 10

Ground cover textures start next. First, a coat of PVA wood glue is painted over the landform where we want grass textures to be applied. A mixture of fine turfs from the Skale Scenics range is then dusted over the glue covered areas to create a base layer of green grass. It looks a little flat at this point though.

STEP 11

To add depth and texture multiple layers of static grasses and fine turfs are applied on top of the first layer of ground cover. Before doing this, remove any excess material from the first application once the glue has dried and then apply a coat of PVA glue mixed with water in a 70:30 ratio. Additional layers can be added by further diluting the PVA glue mixture to allow it to more freely flow into the previously applied grasses.

STEP 12

Completing the look are coarse turf and fine turf fixed in place with matt varnish together with clumps of foliage around the tunnel mouth to bed it in place. More can be added to this scene including details such as lineside flowers and fencing.

WAGONS ROLL FOR 2016

With 60 new wagons including brand new models on the cards for the year ahead, there will be plenty of goods vehicles on hand to expand your Hornby collection.

Headlining the 2016 wagon range are brand new models of the London Midland & Scottish Railway (LMS) 20ton coke hopper along with the Maunsell and Bulleid designed Southern Railway (SR) 10ton cattle wagons. They join an extensive list of new goods wagons extending to 52 vehicles planned for release in the next 12 months.

The LMS 20ton coke hopper was introduced in 1930 with further batches being built by BR to three different diagrams after nationalisation.

In total the LMS built 200 wagons with a further 600 built by private owners. BR construction, taking place at Shildon in the North East, added a further 2,000 vehicles to the coke wagon fleet.

The vehicles went through numerous design modifications during their careers including fitment with wooden or metal

The LMS 20ton coke wagons had a metal body with wooden raves. *Hornby Archive.*

A 3D render of the design work for the new BR diagram 1/151 20ton coke wagon with steel ends and wooden side raves.

A 3D render of the design work for the new LMS diagram 1729 20ton coke wagon with wooden raves all round.

raves, sheet metal ends with side raves and even full height steel bodies. The vehicles were tall at 11ft from rail to the top of the hopper to allow them to carry enough coke to make up their 20ton capacity. Withdrawals started in the 1970s with the last withdrawn in 1981.

Hornby's brand new model of the 20ton coke wagon will cover two different designs – the original LMS diagram 1729 hoppers and the BR diagram

1/151 hoppers. The LMS version is distinct in having wooden raves around both the sides and ends while the BR vehicle had sheet metal ends with wooden side raves – the latter being the most common version with 1,150 being built between 1951 and 1958.

On release two versions of the LMS wagon will be produced as solo vehicles together with two solo BR wagons. A triple pack will also be released containing three of the BR diagram wagons.

Southern cattle

Joining the coke wagon is a new model of the standard Southern Railway 10ton cattle wagon. These were introduced from 1930 to the original Maunsell design, Diagram 1529, to replace ageing pre-grouping vehicles and this was modified by Bulleid in the mid-1940s to create the 1947 introduced Diagram 1530 10ton cattle wagon.

The design used an all steel 10ft 6in chassis with

eight-shoe vacuum brakes and Maunsell brake gear in its original form while the Bulleid vehicles went on to feature plywood ends with metal reinforcement and a repositioned brake lever at the extreme end of the wagon.

The first 150 Bulleid designed wagons were built by the Southern Railway with the remaining 150 from the order constructed after nationalisation under British Railways. They ☞

Stanier '8F' 48060 leads a long rake of LMS diagram 1729 20ton coke hoppers at Wath Road Junction on June 17 1957. These wagons are to be produced as a new product in 2016.
B.W.L Brooksbank.

Hornby is working on new models of both the Maunsell and Bulleid 10ton Southern Railway cattle wagons. This is a Maunsell diagram 1529 vehicle. Mike King.

roamed right across the Southern Railway network from Ashford to Exeter, although a rapid decline in cattle traffic in the BR era saw their work diminish rapidly.

Hornby's new model of the SR cattle wagon will cover the Maunsell Diagram 1529 and Bulleid Diagram 1530 vehicles. Both versions will be released in Southern Railway and British Railways liveries.

Reliveries

Hornby's wide range of goods wagons is being used to good effect with a further 52 new vehicles joining the eight models planned across the new coke and cattle wagons.

Highlights amongst the listing include new versions of the BR 20ton hopper and LMS horsebox – both of which debuted in 2015 – together with a 'Rudd' in Mainline blue, Blue Spot fish vans in late 1960s light blue, shunters trucks for Stoke Gifford and Fowey, the return of the Railfreight VIX and VJX Ferry vans and much more.

As with previous year's a series of private owner liveries suitable for recreating the colourful coal trains of the 1930s and 1940s pre-nationalisation railway will be released too. This willl be on the three, four, five, six and seven plank wooden bodied wagons.

For the full list of new wagon releases see Table 1 and visit *www.hornby.com* for more information. Ⓗ

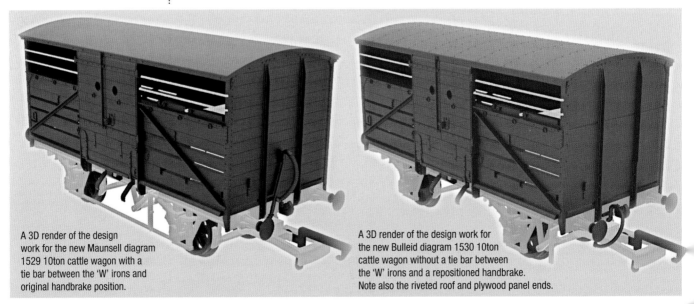

A 3D render of the design work for the new Maunsell diagram 1529 10ton cattle wagon with a tie bar between the 'W' irons and original handbrake position.

A 3D render of the design work for the new Bulleid diagram 1530 10ton cattle wagon without a tie bar between the 'W' irons and a repositioned handbrake. Note also the riveted roof and plywood panel ends.

TABLE 1 – NEW WAGONS 2016

Vehicle	Description	Period	Cat No.
BR 20ton hopper	E252179, BR grey	1950s/1960s	R6725
BR 20ton hopper	E303821, BR grey	1950s/1960s	R6676
LMS horsebox	42489, LMS red	1930s/1940s	R6727
LMS horsebox	42442, LMS red	1930s/1940s	R6727A
LMS horsebox	M42367M, BR crimson	1950s	R6728
LMS horsebox	M42253M, BR crimson	1950s	R6728A
PGA hopper	ARC roadstone	1980s	R6781
BR 20ton hopper (triple pack)	B413757, B413758, B413759, BR grey	1960s/1970s	R6782
PGA hopper	14234, VTG	1980s	R6760
HAA hopper	356618, BR Railfreight	1980s/1990s	R6761
ZBA 'Rudd'	DB972328, Mainline blue	1990s	R6763
BR Insul-fish van	E87438, BR white	1950s/1960s	R6762
LNER extra-long CCT	1274, LNER teak	1930s/1940s	R6682D
LNER extra-long CCT	E1359E, BR crimson	1950s/1960s	R6683D
Three-plank open wagon	Port Talbot Steel Co Ltd	1930s/1940s	R6739
Three-plank open wagon	North British	1930s/1940s	R6740
Three-plank open wagon	Morten and Storer	1930s/1940s	R6741
Three-plank open wagon	Jas Turner and Sons	1930s/1940s	R6742
GWR 'Toad' brake van	W68724, BR grey	1950s/1960s	R6766
BR blue spot fish van	E87128, BR light blue	1960s	R6759
BR blue spot fish van	E87129, BR light blue	1960s	R6759A
BR blue spot fish van	E87130, BR light blue	1960s	R6759B
GWR shunters truck	DW94884, Stoke Gifford, BR grey	1950s/1960s	R6643E
GWR shunters truck	94990, Fowey, GWR grey	1930s/1940s	R6642D
BR 20ton brake van	B954735, RES red and grey	1990s	R6765
Seven-plank open wagon	Gregory	1930s/1940s	R6755
Seven-plank open wagon	Park Gate	1930s/1940s	R6756
Seven-plank open wagon	Richard White and Sons	1930s/1940s	R6757
Seven-plank open wagon	Arthur Wharton	1930s/1940s	R6758
BR 20ton coke wagon	**TBA**	**1930s**	**R6731**
BR 20ton coke wagon	**TBA**	**1930s**	**R6731A**
BR 20ton coke wagon	**TBA**	**1950s**	**R6733**
BR 20ton coke wagon	**TBA**	**1950s**	**R6733A**
BR 20ton coke wagon (triple pack)	**TBA**	**1950s**	**R6783**
SR 10ton cattle wagon	**TBA**	**1930s**	**R6735**
SR 10ton cattle wagon	**TBA**	**1950s**	**R6735A**
SR 10ton cattle wagon	**TBA**	**1930s**	**R6737**
SR 10ton cattle wagon	**TBA**	**1950s**	**R6737A**
Four-plank open wagon	Westleigh Stone and Lime Co Ltd	1930s/1940s	R6743
Four-plank open wagon	North Bitchburn Coal Co Ltd	1930s/1940s	R6744
Four-plank open wagon	Hingley and Sons Ltd	1930s/1940s	R6745
Four-plank open wagon	Stephens and Co	1930s/1940s	R6746
Five-plank open wagon	Walter Burt	1930s/1940s	R6747
Five-plank open wagon	Foster Wilson	1930s/1940s	R6748
Five-plank open wagon	Farndon	1930s/1940s	R6749
Five-plank open wagon	Shap Tarred Granite	1930s/1940s	R6750
Six-plank open wagon	Cadbury Bournville	1930s/1940s	R6751
Six-plank open wagon	Cory Brothers and Co	1930s/1940s	R6752
Six-plank open wagon	Corker and Bevan	1930s/1940s	R6753
Six-plank open wagon	London Brick Company	1930s/1940s	R6754
BR 'Tope' ballast hopper	DB970167, 'Dutch' grey and yellow	1990s	R6764
SR 20ton brake van	55912, Southern Railway brown with red oxide ends	1930s/1940s	R6767
LMS 20ton brake van	730159, LMS bauxite	1940s	R6768
20ton tank wagon	203, Industrial Alcohol	1940s	R6769
14ton tank wagon	24, Carless Petrol	1940s	R6780
PCA tank wagon	TRL10520, Mineral Industries Ltd	1980s/1990s	R6771
100ton bogie tank wagon	TBA		R6772
BR VIX Ferry Van	2380 251.5, BR Railfreight grey	1980s	R6773
BR VJX Ferry Van	B787124, BR Railfreight grey, weathered	1980s	R6774
SR 12ton ventilated van	44811, Southern Railway bauxite	1940s	R6775
Conflat and BD container	B709504, BR bauxite with container 7338, BR crimson	1950s/1960s	R6776

Simple wagon loads

Enhancing your Hornby models doesn't have to be difficult. Martin Howard shows a simple method for creating removable coal wagon loads suitable for any type of open wagon.

It's the detail that really counts when it comes to railway modelling and while there are many projects which will need working up to, there are plenty of simple projects which can enhance items of rolling stock which are well within the grasps of even the newest modeller.

One of the easiest is creating wagon loads and here we'll show how to create a simple but effective removable coal load. The railways were fuelled literally and commercially by coal for many decades and were responsible for the movement of loaded and empty wagons - so this project, which uses packing foam as its basis, is a convenient way of representing full and empty wagons.

The materials used in this project are readily available and your local model retailer will have a plentiful selection of different coal products on hand too. The other ingredient here is simply PVA wood glue together with a couple of plastic containers.

The step by step guide explains how we went about creating this model enhancing load. The method can be used to add coal, ballast, iron ore and other types of mineral loads to suit different wagon styles – all you have to do to create more removable loads is cut the foam to shape to suit the vehicle.

STEP **BY** STEP — MAKING SIMPLE COAL WAGON LOADS

STEP 1
All you need are an empty wagon, a strip of packing foam and a tub of realistic coal. A pair of scissors is the only tool required to make these loads.

STEP 2
Having cut the foam to length to fit the wagon it is clear that the top of the foam needs shaping to fit below the top of the wagon sides and look realistic.

STEP 3
Using scissors, the top face of the foam was sculptured to give it the right shape. Two distinct humps suggest that the coal for this wagon has been loaded in two heaps.

STEP 4
A small amount of neat PVA wood glue is poured into a plastic container and the newly shaped foam is then dipped into it so that only the upper face is covered.

With the coal load in place it is difficult to spot that it is actually removable. The wagon on the right has a permanent fixed coal load created by loading the wagon with coal and applying diluted PVA glue in a 50:50 ratio with water.

STEP **BY** STEP ✎ MAKING SIMPLE COAL WAGON LOADS

STEP 5
With the upper face of the foam fully covered with PVA glue, it is ready for the next step. Using a second plastic tray with crushed coal filling it, the upper face of the foam is pressed into the contents so that the glue can pick up the material.

STEP 6
With the foam lifted from the tray, the coal has been attracted to the surface of the load. The white glue will dry clear, making it invisible on the finished item while the grey colour of the foam helps disguise its own existence.

STEP 7
The load now needs to be set aside to dry thoroughly overnight before being added to the wagon. It may shed a handful of coal pieces, but that won't spoil the finished effect.

STEP 8
After drying completely the load was added to the 21ton mineral wagon ready to take its place in a freight formation. At any time the load can easily be removed to allow this wagon to run empty, meaning that fewer wagons are needed to represent loaded and empty trains.

Selective weathering goes a long way towards recreating the appearance of a real working locomotive. Subtle, understated touches such as the weathering patterns on the roof and the build-up of oil on the underframes are what makes a difference to the finished model.

WEATHERING WITH
Humbrol

Hornby's Class 50 is a brilliant model of these popular engines. TIM SHACKLETON shows how you can make it even more lifelike using readily available Humbrol paints and washes.

To many people, weathering means dirtying up their locomotives and rolling stock. To me, that's only part of the story. In my view, effective weathering is more concerned with bringing models to life and suggesting the build-up over time of the effects of wind, rain, sunlight, smoke, oil, corrosion and other elements. Even an otherwise clean locomotive will bear the marks of the work it does, the fuel it uses, the type of traffic it hauls and the environment in which it operates. The same applies to every aspect of a model railway – track, buildings, signals, road vehicles, even scenery.

Weathering has become all the more popular in recent years, but there are still strong camps for and against the process. It's all down to personal taste and you don't have to treat all your models this way, but I feel that not to do

so is to miss out on an important element of realism. Weathering is also hugely enjoyable and, just as importantly, something we can all do – especially if we focus first on the basics. When you're first starting out you don't need to have expensive equipment or even much by way of artistic skill. What you must have, however, is patience, a good eye for your subject and the willingness to take things one step at a time.

Convincing weathering comes through the gradual building up of effects, and above all acquiring the ability to look really hard at the prototype and copy what you see (made-up weathering effects never look right). Restraint and discretion are equally essential – in weathering your railway models, understatement is everything. Blasting away with an airbrush until your model is thickly coated in filth is not the way to do it!

To show you some of the core techniques, I'm going to take a Hornby Class 50 and work on it using a carefully chosen selection of Humbrol products. I've been weathering railway models for more than 50 years now and if there's one thing I've learned, it's

that there are always new ways to weather railway models and new products available to help you. But until you can use basic paints and powders sensitively, simply and effectively, no miracle product or innovative technique is going to help you master the art. ☞

WHAT WE USED

Product	Type	Cat No.
Matt Leather	Acrylic	62
Brick Red	Acrylic	70
Ocean Grey	Acrylic	106
Dirty Black	Acrylic	RC401
Satin Varnish	Acrylic	135
Matt Leather	Enamel	62
Satin Black	Enamel	85
Dark Grey	Enamel wash	AV0204
Dark Brown	Enamel wash	AV0205
Blue Grey	Enamel wash	AV0206
Gloss Oil Stain	Enamel wash	AV0209
Black	Weathering powder	AV0001
Dark Earth	Weathering powder	AV0007

USEFUL LINKS
Hornby Hobbies   *www.hornby.com*
Humbrol   *www.humbrol.com*

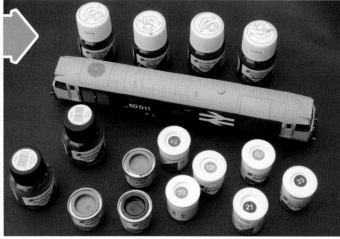

STEP 1

'Large logo' blue suited the Class 50s very well and has always been a popular choice for models. Its visual impact was strong enough to be sustained even when the locomotives were in less than pristine condition.

STEP 2

I use all kinds of materials for weathering – enamel and acrylic paints, weathering powders and enamel washes. They all have their uses but only experience tells you which is the best to use in particular circumstances. Fortunately, experimenting is all part of the fun!

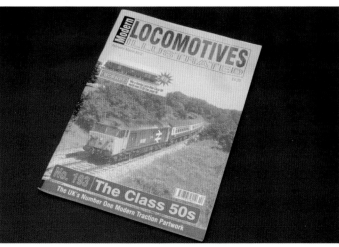

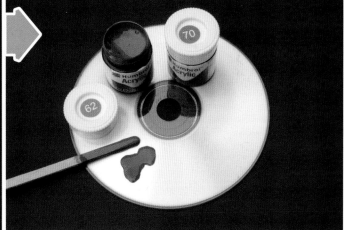

STEP 3

I always work from photographs of the prototype. A lot has been published on the '50s' so you don't have to look hard for information and inspiration. Key Publishing's *Modern Locomotives Illustrated* is an ideal reference source.

STEP 4

With a diesel or electric locomotive, a good place to start is with the wheels. Although the treads are bright the wheel centres are always thickly coated in a mixture of corrosion and ochre-coloured brake-block dust. No. 62 Matt Leather is too light to represent this accurately, while No. 70 Brick Red is too dark. Mixed together in roughly equal parts they look just right. A discarded CD-ROM makes an excellent palette.

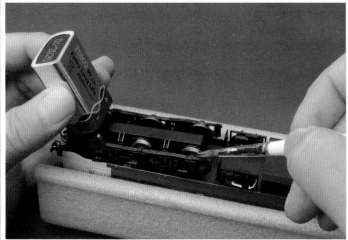

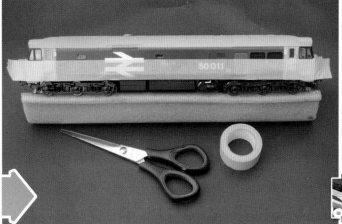

STEP 5

The easiest way to brush paint the wheels is with the model inverted in a foam cradle – this is an offcut of the protective packaging in which a kitchen worktop was delivered. Turn the wheels over under power using a 9v battery and be sure to clean the wheel treads afterwards. The advantage of using acrylic paint is that it dries very quickly, so you can soon move on to the next stage.

STEP 6

I'm going to weather the bogies and underframe using an airbrush which, in this kind of application, gives a much smoother finish than hand brushing. To stop overspray getting everywhere, I've masked off the lower bodysides. Masking tape is readily available from model shops. Once again I'm using the foam cradle, this time with the locomotive tilted back in it so I can get right in close on the running gear.

STEP BY STEP — WEATHERING WITH HUMBROL PAINTS AND WASHES

Step 7

Weathering looks much more convincing when you use a succession of colours to build up tone. Starting with the same Leather/Brick Red mix as before, I've added a 50% tint of Dirty Black (RC 401) and made an initial light pass along the underframe, spraying from a distance of no more than an inch (25mm). With acrylics I use a paint:thinners mix of about 80:20.

STEP 8

I've varied the proportions of the three colours to add further shades, once again using just enough paint to make a difference. Weathering on a locomotive is rarely even or monochromatic, although the differences are not marked. There are no hard edges, which is why an airbrush is so useful.

STEP 9

Finally we can pull back the masking tape to reveal the heavily discoloured bogies. Even so, this is only the beginning. Weathering is all about added layers, trying to create the effect of dirt build-up over time.

STEP 10

Next we move on to the roof. The area around the exhausts is always the first to get dirty – even on a freshly painted locomotive, this part will become heavily sooted within hours. Here I've used a straightforward coat of Dirty Black, airbrushed from close range. We mostly see our models from above, so it makes sense to put in an extra effort with the roof area.

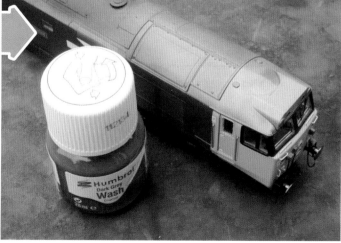

STEP 11

Using low pressure (about 18psi) I'm wafting a thin mist of Dirty Black over other parts of the roof to suggest general blackening and toning down of the grey paintwork. The visiting card helps maintain a straight edge and stops paint getting on the bodysides.

STEP 12

Switching now to enamel washes, I've hand brushed the areas that I want to remain grey. Washes are designed to be taken off immediately afterwards, leaving a residue in out-of-the-way places. This gives a subtle discoloration and also helps to define depth by suggesting shadows where there aren't any.

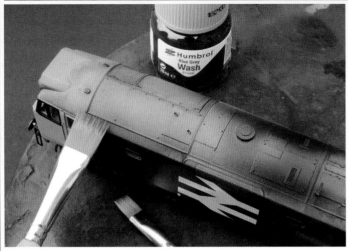

STEP 13

To create a variation in tone I started with a Dark Grey wash and then coloured smaller areas with Blue Grey. Dipping a flat brush in clean enamel thinners, I can then lightly stroke the wet paint with a downward movement to suggest rain washing down the roof and taking some of the weathering with it.

STEP 14

Finally I airbrushed the lighter parts of the roof with a fine coat of Ocean Grey acrylic (No. 106) to soften any visible edges and blend the overall roof weathering together. I wanted to recreate the effect of layers of weathering building up from different sources – paint fade, exhaust sooting, rain streaks and so on.

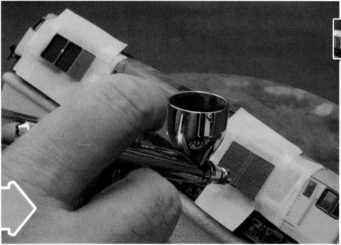

STEP 15

To finish, a touch of AW001 Black weathering powder around the exhaust ports to suggest the heavy sooting that always builds up there. From photographs you can see how the grey roofs gradually blackened and became discoloured. Some of the '50s' in 'large logo' livery – 50002/3/6/8/11/14/16/24/27/28/42/43/46/47/49 – eventually got black or dark grey roofs to try and disguise this.

STEP 16

The various grilles and louvres on a diesel attract dirt build-up. Rather than try and paint them freehand, it's probably better to mask off the surrounding bodywork and use an airbrush to spray on a fine mist of the same dark weathering mix we used on the bogies.

> To be weathered a model needn't look absolutely filthy – in fact heavy weathering is rarely convincing unless done by a master of the art.

STEP BY STEP   WEATHERING WITH HUMBROL PAINTS AND WASHES

STEP 17

Thanks to the effort that's been put in on the underframe, roof and bodysides, the Class 50 is already starting to look a bit more workmanlike. None of the weathering, however, is in any way heavy. Successful weathering is all about the gentle build-up of effects, all of them complementing one another.

STEP 18

One of the key areas on a diesel where dirt builds up is the tumblehome, the curved section of the lower bodyside. Mechanical washers can't normally reach this space, so it becomes covered in oil, track dirt and brake block dust. I'm airbrushing freehand but it might be advisable to use the 'business card' method here to protect other areas from overspray.

STEP 19

It may be preferable to use enamel paints for this stage of the weathering. They dry much more slowly than acrylics and this is useful if you need to work the paint with brushes to create particular effects.

STEP 20

I'm using a wide, flat brush dipped in thinners to create a subtle streaking effect that mimics the way rainwater washes real-life weathering down the sides of locomotives and carriages. Subtlety is everything – it's very easy to overdo this effect! Make sure the streaks are vertical.

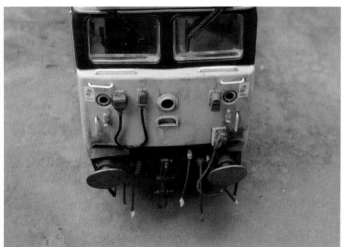

STEP 21

Whatever state the bodysides get into, the yellow front end of a diesel is normally kept clean – it's a vital safety feature, helping track workers gauge the distance of an approaching train. Cab windows are also cleaned regularly – pronounced 'wiper marks' are a bit of a modelling cliché, and are rarely seen on the prototype. A thin brownish wash is all you need to bring out the relief detail and add a little gentle discoloration.

STEP 22

With weathering it's the little details that count. I've used a hint of Dark Earth weathering powder on the bogies to suggest road dirt thrown up from the track and mingling with the ever present brake block dust and oil spillage. I'll also run a thin wash of dark brown-grey in the door handle recesses and around the handrails.

STEP 23
Spilled fuel around the tank area is represented by a wash of Gloss Oil Stain, with a couple of neatly-defined streaks of Satin Black enamel (85).

STEP 24
These small details can only really be done by hand. An airbrush is a fantastic tool for use in weathering but hand brushing techniques have a valuable place too. I have no preferences either way, and use whatever is best suited to the job in hand.

STEP 25
If you want to give your model a new identity, tampo-printed names and numbers are easily removed by rubbing them with a wooden cocktail stick sharpened to a chisel shape. This won't damage the bodywork – but be careful not to rub too hard!

STEP 26
I used Railtec transfers and Extreme Etchings nameplates to turn *Centurion* into *Temeraire*. Always replace the whole of a numberset, not just a few characters. The originals might be a slightly different size, or the typefaces might not quite match – the discrepancy is usually obvious. You can glue the etched nameplates in position, but I prefer a few spots of paint in the same colour as the bodysides.

STEP 27
The final step was to brush-paint the bodysides with acrylic satin varnish. This gives a convincing gleam and suggests a well-cleaned, working locomotive. The roof, however, is almost dead flat while the underframe glistens with oil and spilled fuel. Real life locomotives are full of contrasts like this. Note that both sides of the locomotive are similar in terms of weathering patterns, but far from identical!

TIM SHACKLETON

As well as his regular weathering articles in *Hornby Magazine*, Tim Shackleton has written five books on the subject, made two DVDs and led many weathering courses for modellers at Missenden Abbey and Pendon Museum.

Using a selection of products from the Humbrol range and applying them with care and reference to photographs of Class 50s in large logo blue livery results in a model which looks like a working locomotive – enhancing the fine detail of the product.

Ballasting for beginners

Ballast is an essential part of the real railway for track stability and drainage, but in model form it is purely cosmetic. Martin Howard explains how realistic ballasting can be achieved in 12 simple steps.

Almost every railway needs ballast to secure the track in position and in model form we can represent this in a number of ways. At one end of the scale is foam underlay stretching through pre-ballasted foams and plastic base track with moulded ballast to the ultimate hand re-produced ballasting.

Loose ballasting is what we are going to show how to achieve here. This method can be used to represent in detail how the real railway is held in place, creating realistic 'shoulders' either side of the track and allowing it to be coloured to closely mimic that of the real railway.

The materials are readily available from model shops and for this project we have used a combination of ballasts from the Hornby Skale Scenics range using the fine grades throughout for preference. Different ballast manufacturers offer different grades, so careful selection is required.

To properly replicate the detail of a ballasted railway we also need to tone down the track to set it into the scene. For this project this has been done by simply spray painting the track with Humbrol No. 29 from an aerosol can. Two precautions are essential for this method: the first is a well ventilated room and the second is ensuring that all the point blades are covered with masking tape. If the latter is ignored, you will spend a lot of time cleaning paint out of the points to make them work again.

Moving to the process of ballasting this is done by spreading ballast onto the track formation and then brushing it into place with a ½in paintbrush. This latter stage takes time, but it is rewarded with the end result of perfectly positioned ballast.

Now though we need to fix it in place, which calls for a method which has been used countless thousands of times

by model builders across the world. It involves diluting PVA glue with water to 50:50 ratio, adding a couple of drops of detergent to the mixture to take the surface tension off the water and applying it to the previously prepared ballast with a syringe. An important step before applying the glue is to lightly wet – but not soak – the ballast with a water mister as this will allow the glue to flow more freely into the ballast whilst also holding it in position.

The final stage is to introduce further weathering to the track. We did this with multiple applications of heavily diluted dark brown and black water based paints. They soak into the ballast to tint rather than colour it, enhancing the effect of the previous weathering on the rails and sleepers.

Ballasting track isn't the quickest part of a model project, but the results are well worth the effort and speak for themselves. ☞

STEP BY STEP — LOOSE BALLASTING

STEP 1
To begin the process of ballasting this track formation first we need to tone down the track to take the shine off the rail sides. Step one is to cover the delicate point blades with masking tape so that paint cannot penetrate these areas.

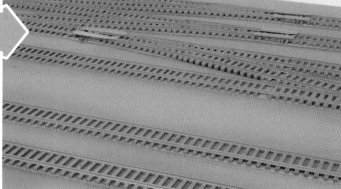

STEP 2
As a quick and efficient means of toning down the track Humbrol No. 29 from a spray can is sprayed over the entire track formation. This takes the shine off the rail sides and colours the sleepers and the cork underneath the track to good effect.

STEP 3

With the paint now dry – acrylics take little more than 30 minutes to be touch dry – the track formation already looks more realistic. However, the process of spraying the track means that the rail heads have also been coloured - which we need to rectify if trains are to run.

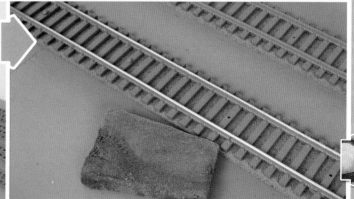

STEP 4

Using a track rubber – we always use an old one for heavy duty cleaning like this – all of the rail heads are cleaned of paint and the layout checked for operation again. This takes time, but is a step not to be missed out.

STEP **BY** STEP LOOSE BALLASTING

STEP 5

A combination of Skale Scenics ballasts were selected and mixed together in a plastic tub ready for application to the layout. The process of mixing different ballast colours helps improve the look of a layout. If possible try introducing fine grades in small quantities to further vary the ballast.

STEP 6

Ballast is spread over the track formation loose and roughly in position. This isn't ready for gluing in place yet as the ballast is much too messy.

STEP 7

Using a ½in paintbrush, the loose ballast is manoeuvred into position between the sleepers and either side of the track to create a realistic look to the ballast – we're aiming for the effect of the nearest track with those behind still waiting for the ballast to be brushed into place. This takes time, but is well worth it.

STEP 8

With all the ballast neatly brushed into place the whole area to be glued needs to be lightly wetted with water from a water mister. This stops the ballast moving during application of the glue and also helps the glue flow into the loose ballast.

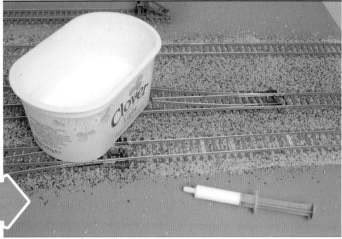

STEP 9

One final step before moving onto applying the glue – add a couple of drops of model oil around the moving parts of points to stop the glue seizing them up.

STEP 10

Now we are ready to apply the glue. PVA wood glue has been diluted to a 50:50 ratio with water in a plastic container. A couple of drops of detergent have been added to remove surface tension from the water which will help it flow into the loose ballast smoothly. Mix it together thoroughly.

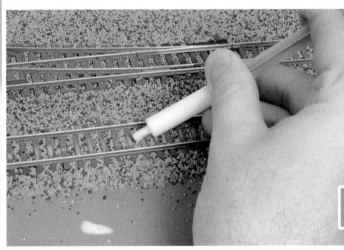

STEP 11

Using a small syringe, load up the previously mixed glue into its barrel and then transfer it to the layout. We prefer to apply glue down the centre of the track first as it will gradually move out to the sides to fix all the ballast in place. Ensure adequate coverage and then leave to dry for at least 24 hours.

STEP 12

Having completed all the physical ballasting, it looks smart but too fresh for a working railway. If you want to go further you can add washes of water based dark brown and black paints thinned with water to the track formations to tint the ballast for a more realistic finish. Ultimately we added a further wash of black followed by a second wash of brown to create the final look for the track using a 1/4in paint brush.

The LNER 'Q6' 0-8-0

Throughout the history of the railways there has always been a demand for reliable, simple and powerful freight engines. Evan Green-Hughes discovers the story of Vincent Raven's hugely successful 'Q6' 0-8-0s.

At the beginning of the 20th century industry in Britain was expanding at an unprecedented rate causing a demand for raw materials which the railways struggled to meet. In the North East the concentration of coal mines, ports and steel-making plants brought particular problems in this respect and required vast increases in tonnages to be worked.

The North Eastern Railway (NER) badly needed more powerful locomotives to haul these trains, particularly around Durham and for the coal traffic from South Yorkshire to the docks at Hull and as a result Wilson Worsdell had introduced a heavy 0-8-0 tender engine in which the whole weight of the locomotive was available for adhesion and braking.

This class, the 'Q5', had a relatively light axle load and a good steam brake and when fitted with piston valves proved to be a very reliable addition to the fleet. A total of 90 were built between 1901 and 1911 and they were very successful.

So rapid was the growth of traffic that the NER then took the unprecedented step of electrifying the line between Shildon and Newport but even with this route turned over to electric traction more heavy freight steam locomotives were still required. By this time Vincent Raven had succeeded Wilson Worsdell as Chief Mechanical Engineer and he decided that the need could be satisfied by improving the 'Q5'.

New design

As a result he created a new design which incorporated the frames, cylinders and mechanical arrangement of the earlier engines but with a larger superheated boiler. The firebox was made six inches longer to cope with the bigger boiler and these changes meant the complete locomotive was 1ft longer than its predecessor.

As might be expected given its parentage the improved locomotive, known as the 'T2' by the NER but later as the 'Q6' to the London and North Eastern Railway (LNER), was an unqualified success and proved popular amongst enginemen and operating staff.

Construction began at Darlington Works in 1913 and the class emerged from there at a steady rate until 1919 when production was contracted to the Armstrong Whitworth plant at Newcastle, finally ending in 1921. Unlike many other classes the ☞

With a mixed rake including steel plate wagons and BR 16ton mineral wagons behind 'Q6' 0-8-0 63387 passes Billingham with a West Hartlepool-Tyne Yard goods on August 22 1967 – the final year of service for the 'Q6' class. Mike Fox/Rail Archive Stephenson.

LNER 'Q6' STATISTICS

Designer:	Vincent Raven
Built:	1913-1921
Total in class:	120
Withdrawn:	1960-1967
Builder:	North Eastern Railway, Darlington Armstrong Whitworth, Newcastle
Purpose:	Heavy freight
Power classification:	6F
Wheel arrangement:	0-8-0
Weight (locomotive):	65tons 18cwt
Weight (tender):	44tons 2cwt
Driving wheel diameter:	4ft 71/4in
Wheelbase (including tender):	42ft 73/4in
Boiler:	Parallel, 5ft 6in diameter
Boiler pressure:	180psi
Cylinders:	Two, outside, 20in x 26in
Tractive effort:	28,800lbs

'Q6s' needed little modification, with the only major changes made being to the boiler. In 1916 Raven altered the arrangement of the tubes and reduced the number from 146 to 90 so a higher level of superheat could be obtained. He also gradually increased the boiler pressure from its initial 160psi to 175psi and finally to 180psi to increase power. When replacement boilers became necessary in the late 1920s the replacements had 131 tubes and then 134. Boilers built from '1938 onwards had the dome positioned slightly further to the rear due to differences in the way they were constructed.

In August 1946 the Ministry of Transport authorised the LNER to convert 450 of its heavy freight engines to oil burning and in anticipation changes were made to the superheater elements. However the project did not proceed and all engines continued to burn coal for the rest of their careers.

Three different types of tender were provided new on the 'Q6s' and two more types were used during their lifetimes due to swaps with other classes. The original tender was the 3,940gallon type which held five tons of coal, but some class members received

a 3,669gallon version previously issued to 'C7' 4-4-2s and these had higher sides. Other engines were given 4,125gallon versions which had also been used with 'C7s' while 2213-2232 had this style from new, but with an improved self-trimming coal space. There were also differences in coal rail design and water scoop apparatus was fitted in some cases. There was a great deal of exchange of tenders between ex-NER locomotives in the early days of the LNER and this resulted in examples of all styles being fitted to the class in British Railways days.

In traffic

On introduction to service the first 20 locomotives were split between West Auckland shed in County Durham and Dairycoates shed in Hull and then the next batch of 10 were shared between Hull and Tyne Dock. Electric locomotives soon displaced the 'Q6s' from much of the work at West Auckland, after which they became widely dispersed throughout the system.

In 1920 the class could be found at 11 sheds, including Tyne Dock, Carlisle, Leeds Neville Hill, Hull Dairycoates and Stockton. They were mainly employed

The 'Q6' fleet was used on some of the most challenging gradients in the North East at the head of heavy freight trains. Travelling at barely more than walking pace 63343 presents a dramatic spectacle as it passes Beamish with coal train for Consett in May 1964. W.J. Verden Anderson/Rail Archive Stephenson.

The driver leans from the cab of NER 'Q6' 0-8-0 2277 as it coasts down grade near Plawsworth with a coke train on August 28 1937. James Clark/ Rail Archive Stephenson.

Carrying standard unlined LNER black livery Raven 'Q6' 2262 rests at York shed in 1935. Gordon Hepburn/Rail Archive Stephenson.

on heavy coal trains from the collieries to bulk users such as steelworks, on limestone traffic, aggregates and steel trains. Other duties included working from Hull to Manchester via the Woodhead route, Immingham to Yorkshire and regular runs into the Doncaster area. During the depression of the early 1930s some engines were laid up for lack of work with several being stored at Darlington in this period, usually after works repair.

In 1938 the LNER introduced a scheme to concentrate particular classes at as few sheds as possible and as a consequence

some places such as Stockton and Selby lost their allocation. By the following year only 10 depots still had 'Q6s' with the majority being at Hull, Gateshead Borough Gardens, Newport and Blaydon. Their duties remained largely unchanged however. During 1943 a further reduction was made to the number of sheds which had 'Q6s' and no less than 50 were then allocated to Newport in the Darlington area and 30 to Leeds Neville Hill with all the others at Hull Dairycoates, Stockton, Consett, Selby and Borough Gardens. This proved to be a move too far as the locomotives

were then shedded in places inconvenient for their duties and consequently most of the Neville Hill allocation was sent further north to places like Darlington and Consett.

During the war years the class ventured further afield and made frequent visits to Edinburgh on goods work, but were viewed with some disdain by the Scottish enginemen who by that time had become used to modern mixed traffic engines such as the 'V2' 2-6-2 and therefore nicknamed the 'Q6s' 'belly-crawlers'. The class also regularly worked to Peterborough and March and

was used extensively on the East Coast Main Line south of Doncaster for the first time. They also reached the Cheshire Lines and Liverpool. However with the end of the war the 'Q6s' were once again concentrated on their traditional traffic in the North East with most being based in County Durham or Teesside and still used on heavy freight and mineral trains. Many were reallocated to the new steam 'super shed' at Thornaby when it opened in 1958.

An unusual transfer was that of two 'Q6s', 63355 and 63373 to Kirkby Stephen in 1955 where they were required for heavy 🖝

2241 is barely two years old as it passes Croft Spa with an Up coal train at 6.20pm on July 17 1920. The NER originally classified the 'Q6s' as 'T2' – the LNER changing their designation to fit in with its classification system. Q respresented eight coupled locomotives without a pony truck. *William Rogerson/Rail Archive Stephenson.*

freight work between there and Tebay, a duty that had previously been carried out by 'Q5s'. The Kippax branch near Leeds, which was heavily graded, also offered regular work for the class which was also favoured for duties involving going up and down Heselden or Seaton banks in the North East. Latterly there was a duty from West Hartlepool to Coxhoe which conveyed dolomite in containers and 'Q6s' were the preferred traction for this very heavy duty.

One traffic for which the 'Q6s' were never used was passenger work and the locomotives were never fitted with train vacuum brake equipment. They were, however, equipped with a single vacuum cylinder to operate the locomotive and the tender brakes. It was the failure of the linkage to this cylinder that caused one of the class to run

'Q6' 63386 pulls away from Woodhorn Colliery with a loaded coal train for the staithes at North Blyth in July 1964. *W.J. Verden Anderson/Rail Archive Stephenson.*

LNER 'Q6' NUMBERING

Built	Builder	LNER 1923	LNER 1946	BR number
1913	NER Darlington	1247-1254	3340-3369	63340-63369
		1257, 1261-1262		
		1264, 1271, 1276, 1278,		
		1280, 1283-1285, 1288,		
		1291-1294, 1311, 1335		
		1361-1363		
1917	NER Darlington	2213-2232	3370-3389	63370-63389
1918	NER Darlington	2233-2242	3390-3399	63390-63399
1919	NER Darlington	2243-2252	3400-3409	63400-63409
	Armstrong Whitworth	2253-2255	3410-3412	63410-63412
1920	Armstrong Whitworth	2256-2298	3413-3455	63413-63455
1921	Armstrong Whitworth	2299-2302	3456-3459	63456-63459

The now preserved 'Q6' 0-8-0 63395 stands in the company of ex-War Department 'Austerity' 2-8-0 90009 at Sunderland South Dock shed on the fresh morning of September 1 1967. *Mike Fox/Rail Archive Stephenson.*

away with a coal train near South Pelaw in 1942. Several other 'Q6s' were involved in accidents or incidents during their working careers. 63395 derailed and turned over on its side in June 1959 near Consett when working from Croft Yard with a goods train and 63355 was seriously derailed at Smardale in May 1955 while running tender first. None of these incidents was sufficiently serious to warrant withdrawal of any of the engines.

The class survived intact for more than 40 years and it was not until 1960 that 63372 became the first to be taken out of service after sustaining damage that was not repaired. General withdrawals started three years later as some duties were transferred to new BR Standard '9F' 2-10-0s and others went to new Class 37 diesels. The pace of withdrawals quickened during the following years and by 1967 all had gone.

Preservation survivor

However this was not the end for the class as the North Eastern Locomotive Preservation Society was successful in buying 63395 when it was withdrawn by British Railways. Work soon started on its restoration at Tyne Dock shed but a few months later the engine was taken to Hartlepool for hydraulic testing. A further move to Thornaby shed was made the following year where the boiler was retubed, hydraulically tested and steamed. Train vacuum braking equipment and carriage steam heating connections were fitted during this period. With this work completed the 'Q6' moved in steam to Grosmont on the North Yorkshire Moors Railway (NYMR) where it arrived in June 1970.

The locomotive was used on passenger trains until late 1971 when it had its large flue tubes replaced and received a mechanical overhaul, emerging in North Eastern Railway black livery as 2238. In this guise it made an appearance at the Shildon celebrations of 1975 before returning to the North Yorkshire Moors where it worked regularly for the next eight years before requiring another overhaul after having covered 11,368 miles.

2238 then remained in store for 18 years, sidelined by its owners who by now had two express engines to look after and it wasn't until 2001 that the boiler was removed from the frames for overhaul. The bottom half of the locomotive was taken to the Preservation Group's new headquarters at Darlington for overhaul while the boiler was repaired by the NYMR under contract with the aid of a grant from the National Lottery.

The mechanical overhaul was completed in 2005 and the boiler returned to the frames at Grosmont the following year. A re-entry to service followed in 2007 and since then the locomotive has been a popular feature at the line. It is currently in service.

The 'Q6s' were simple and rugged locomotives designed for very heavy work. The large boiler ensured that the engines were never short of steam, even when working over steep gradients, while the two large outside cylinders ensured that the steam could be adequately applied to the wheels. With all their weight over the coupled wheels the 'Q6s' were very sure-footed engines which mastered their typical duties. It is a great credit to Sir Vincent Raven that every single one of them survived for more than half a century performing the work which they were designed to do without any form of serious modification and that many of those engines survived to almost the final days of steam. ⊞

11 new locomotives line up for
RAILROAD

The RailRoad range is where a lifetime in railway modelling can start with these entry level products. We preview the new items for 2016.

If you aren't sure where to start when it comes to building up a collection the RailRoad range is the perfect place to begin. Prices designed to suit the average wallet lead this expanding sector of the Hornby portfolio which sees older and less detailed models cascaded from the main range to RailRoad.

The RailRoad range covers everything from freelance industrial locomotives through to giants of the main line including Gresley's famous streamlined 'A4' 4-6-2, the BR 'Deltic' 100mph diesels and even, since 2015, the Crosti-boilered '9F' 2-10-0.

New for this year's collection is the Class 20 – a former Lima model being returned to front line service with RailRoad as well as in the Twin Track Sound section, see pages 96-97. Finished in the popular Railfreight grey livery with red solebar stripe, this will be a neat addition - especially alongside the new version of the Class 08 diesel shunter in Intercity livery and a Class 87 in BR blue. Completing the diesel line-up is 'Warship' D805 *Benbow* in BR green.

Steam is taking a British Railways theme in 2016 with some

RAILROAD LOCOMOTIVES 2016

Class	Description	Period	Cat No.
Class 08 0-6-0	08673, Intercity	1980s/1990s	R3490
Class 20 Bo-Bo	20059, Railfreight grey with red stripe	1980s/1990s	R3492
Class 87 Bo-Bo	87026 *Sir Richard Arkwright*, BR blue	1980s	R3493
Class 42 B-B	D805 *Benbow*, BR green	1950s	R3491
LMS 'Black Five' 4-6-0	45025, BR lined black	1950s	R3494
LNER 'Hunt' 4-4-0	62760 *The Cotswold*, BR lined black, early crests	1950s	R3495
Industrial 0-4-0T	Kelly and Son Paper Mill	1940s	R3496
Class 55 Co-Co	D9016 *Gordon Highlander*, BR two-tone green	1960s	R3497
LMS 'Jinty' 0-6-0T	19, Somerset and Dorset Joint Railway blue	1920s	R3498
GWR 'Hall' 4-6-0	6946 *Heatherden Hall*, BR lined green, late crests	1960s	R3499
BR Crosti '9F' 2-10-0	92021, BR black, early crests, weathered	1960s	R3356

The Class 20 is returning to Hornby's collection in the RailRoad range in 2016 as 20059 in the attractive Railfreight grey livery. On June 22 1985 20010 stands outside Derby Works in ex-works Railfreight colours. Richard Priestley/Railphotoprints.co.uk.

important new arrivals in the form of the Stanier 'Black Five' 4-6-0 as 45025 in BR black with early crests and the LNER 'D49' 4-4-0 – or 'Hunt' – as 62760 *The Cotswold* in the same colour scheme.

The Crosti is back too with a weathered finish offering a superb new choice of heavy freight power while the GWR 'Hall' 4-6-0, first released in 2015, will be refreshed as 6946 *Heatherden Hall* in BR lined green.

Beyond locomotives, new diesel and steam train packs are on the cards for the New Year together with a new triple pack set of private owner wagons and Southern Railway carriages in olive green.

Visit *www.hornby.com* for more on the RailRoad collection. Ⓗ

RAILROAD CARRIAGES AND WAGONS 2016

Vehicle	Description	Period	Cat No.
Open wagons (triple pack)	Triple pack of private owner hopper wagons	1930s/1940s	R6784
SR composite coach	5505, Southern Railway olive green	1930s	R4743
SR brake coach	3563, Southern Railway olive green	1930s	R4744

RAILROAD TRAIN PACKS 2016

Description	Period	Cat No.
Diesel freight pack: LMS liveried Class 08, brown van, LMS coal wagon	1940s	R3488
GWR freight pack: '101' 0-4-0T, 'Toad' brake van, Broadoak wagon	1930s	R3489

Hornby history

For almost 100 years the word Hornby has been synonymous with the best in model railways, a proud tradition that is maintained to the present day. Evan Green-Hughes looks back at its story.

The first trains produced under the Hornby name made their appearance in 1920 when Meccano pioneer Frank Hornby launched his first clockwork train set. This simple model of a four-wheel engine and its carriages was the first of its kind to be aimed at the mass family market at a price they could afford and it was a runaway success with thousands produced. Electric versions followed but they were not as popular as the clockwork models which would continue to dominate the toy market for the next two decades.

All of these trains were produced at the firm's extensive factory at Binns Road in Liverpool and such was the demand for the company's products that at one time this was one of the largest model manufacturing plants in the world. During this period Meccano also began producing its famous range of Dinky Toy model cars and commercial vehicles.

Early Hornby models were built to the scale of 1:48, now known as 'O' gauge, which meant that a large area was needed to lay out all but the most simple of trackplans. This was at a time when the average house was decreasing in size and Hornby realised that in

Hornby Dublo launched in 1938 offering the chance for a true table top railway system. Vectis Auctions.

Reproduction presented with Model Railway Enthusiast

1938-1939

HORNBY-DUBLO TRAINS

THE PERFECT TABLE RAILWAY

Gauge OO

Manufactured by
MECCANO LIMITED
Binns Road, Liverpool 13
7/938/185 U.K.

HORNBY TIMELINE

1920
Meccano launches its first Hornby clockwork trainset

1925
Hornby releases its first electric train set operating from mains power!

1929
A safer 6v DC power supply is introduced for Hornby electric trains

1938
Hornby Dublo three-rail system launches

1959
Hornby Dublo introduces its new two-rail track system

1964
Lines Brothers buy Meccano to create Triang-Hornby brand

1972
Dunbee-Combex-Marx buy Lines Brothers and launch Hornby Railways

1980
Hornby Hobbies launches as the new name for Hornby Railways

1986
Hornby Hobbies became a public limited company

1995
Hornby Hobbies moves all production to China

2003
Hornby launches the first 'OO' ready-to-run live steam locomotives

The annual Hornby catalogue is a highlight of the year for enthusiasts of all ages. *Vectis Auctions.*

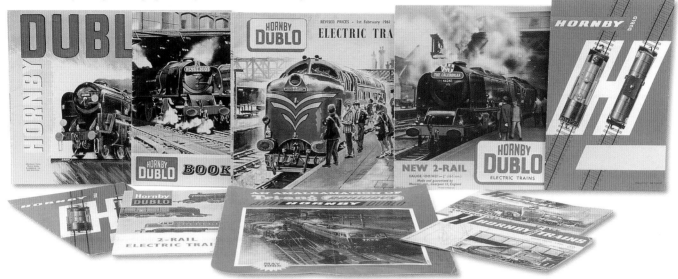

order for the business to be able to expand it would need to produce trains which would be more easily accommodated in a smaller space. As a result a range of models was designed that was half the size of those in production and which was appropriately titled 'Dublo'.

First appearing in 1938 these die-cast metal locomotives and their tinplate carriages were the wonder of their age. For 12s/6d you could own a very reasonable representation of a London and North Eastern Railway (LNER) 'N2' tank engine with clockwork drive but for only 5/- more you could have one with an electric motor. This was a revelation because up to this time an equivalent model was over ten times more expensive than this. Instantly railway modelling was within the budget of the average household and at a size that enabled a reasonable layout to be accommodated indoors. The electric trains used a three-rail system in which the current travelled up an extra track and was picked up by the engine using skates fitted below it.

Hornby Dublo soon added a model of the famous Gresley 'A4' 4-6-2 to the range and this was available in an electric train set for 70/- or with a clockwork motor for 39s 6d. With this release the company established a pattern of producing exciting

and prestigious models which everyone wanted to own.

Increasing realism

Production of the Hornby Dublo range was suspended for the duration of the Second World War and things did not return to normal again until 1948, although by this time the firm had abandoned the production of clockwork models in favour of the more popular electric versions. The range expanded quickly and soon encompassed not only locomotives, carriages and wagons but also stations,

platforms and other buildings. Hornby had become a world leader in its field.

In March 1959 there was another significant advance when Hornby introduced its range of two rail locomotives together with redesigned and more realistic track. The first two-rail locomotive was the pretty 0-6-0T based on the South Eastern and Chatham Railway 'R1' class. This locomotive had a plastic body, unlike many of the others in the range, but was moulded to a high quality specification that was very unusual for its day.

Two rail versions of many of the other locomotives followed in quick succession and before long sales of the upgraded models outpaced those of the traditional three-rail design. It was not long before the decision was taken to drop the original three-rail system altogether and to concentrate on the new format.

In the late 1950s and early 1960s Hornby had a reputation for keeping up with the times. Brand new locomotives such as the English Electric Type 1 (or Class 20) were available in model form sometimes within months of ☞

Early Hornby Dublo locomotives now fetch premium prices. This is pre-war Gresley 'A4' 4498 *Sir Nigel Gresley*. Vectis Auctions.

In the 1950s Hornby gained a high reputation for delivering new models as the new classes were introduced to British Railways. This is the English Electric 'Deltic' which was created from works drawings to coincide with the launch of the real locomotives. *Vectis Auctions.*

Hornby's locomotives reached iconic status with its customers. This is artwork for a 1950s catalogue of a train set containing the highly popular Gresley 'N2' 0-6-2T and a breakdown train. *Vectis Auctions.*

them appearing on the main line, with models being produced from original manufacturer's drawings, with development work taking place even before the prototype had been constructed.

By this time another manufacturer, Tri-ang Trains, was an active and successful competitor to Hornby. Its models were not of such high quality but sold well because they were available more cheaply and this was impacting on the profits of the Hornby organisation. Consequently in 1964 Lines Brothers, the owner of Tri-ang Trains, bought Meccano Ltd and merged the two ranges of trains which were then marketed as Tri-ang-Hornby.

Over a period of time new models were introduced to a higher standard than those previously manufactured by Tri-ang but using plastic moulding techniques. As a result the old Hornby Dublo die-cast models, which were more expensive to manufacture, were withdrawn from sale. Interestingly it was not to be the end for these models as the tools were sold on to other companies, with the result that many of them continued in production under other names for many years to come. Production of 'O' gauge models did, however, cease altogether.

Tri-ang-Hornby continued to expand the range for a further eight years, bringing in some of the most popular models of this period. These included Gresley 'A3' 4-6-2 4472 *Flying Scotsman*, BR '9F' 2-10-0 *Evening Star*, the English Electric Type 3 (later Class 37) and the 'Hymek' diesel, along with a comprehensive range of carriages, wagons and accessories. By today's standards some of the models were quite

While locomotives and rolling stock have always fronted the Hornby range, buildings and structures have been important too. *Vectis Auctions.*

Train sets have always been an important part of Hornby's roster. This is a late 1960s Triang-Hornby Freightmaster set containing a Class 31, a circuit of track and a collection of wagons. *Vectis Auctions.*

crude but they held the general dimensions of the prototype and were extremely popular.

Unfortunately interest in railways was declining in the early 1970s, mainly due to the rundown of the main line system and the replacement of steam by diesel and electric traction. As a result railway modelling was not as popular as it had once been. Tri-ang-Hornby had some difficult years but matters came to crisis point in 1972 when parent company Lines Brothers went out of business. Rescue came in the form of another company, Dunbee-Combex-Marx, which bought the range and relaunched it as Hornby Railways in 1972. The next few years saw more new manufacturers entering the field and Hornby introducing new and upgraded models in an attempt to compete for sales at the scale end of the market.

A new dawn

There was a major innovation in 1979 when Hornby introduced a control system called Zero 1,

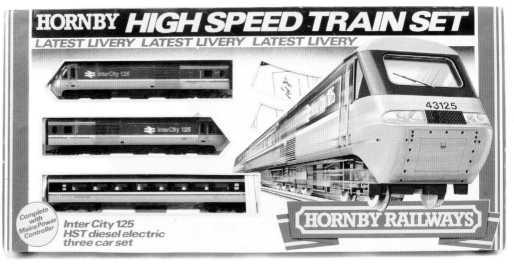

In the 1960s and 1970s the Hornby brand went from Dublo to Tri-ang-Hornby and in 1972 to Hornby Railways. This is one of its popular Inter City 125 train sets from the Hornby Railways period. *Vectis Auctions.*

EVENING STAR

The last steam locomotive built by British Railways

The amalgamation of Tri-ang and Hornby resulted in many spectacular releases including BR's last built steam locomotive – '9F' 2-10-0 92220 *Evening Star*. Vectis Auctions.

many years before anyone else. This was a forerunner of the digital control systems which are in widespread use today and, although it was out of production within ten years, underlined Hornby's place as a leader in the world marketplace.

In 1980 control of the company changed to its own management and from then on it has become known as Hornby Hobbies. A steady programme of upgrades and new models then took place with great success and as a result the company went public in 1986. As well as good quality scale models Hornby also went back to its roots and began to provide models aimed firmly at the first-time modeller, including Thomas the Tank Engine and Harry Potter themed releases.

Hornby has been able to continually expand throughout recent times and one of the ways this has been done has been by buying other manufacturers. Some of the products made by Dapol entered the catalogue in the late 1990s while the popular Lima range was also added, and some of the better ones upgraded with better mechanisms. Airfix, Humbrol and Corgi have also been brought into Hornby Hobbies in recent years to produce a formidable range of complementary products.

Production of the Skaledale range of resin buildings and accessories commenced in

2003 and has proved a very popular addition.

Exacting standards

In recent years Hornby's models have reached higher levels of realism than ever before and have become every bit as good as the best handmade models of the past.

Manufacture in China has improved quality and detail beyond all expectations while the range continues to extend and become more comprehensive. Much of this has been as a

result of improved manufacturing techniques which have made the representation of ever-more intricate detail a reality. However some of these models were not appropriate for younger models due to their level of detail and at the same time were sold at a price which was beyond the reach of those at this end of the market. In answer to this Hornby introduced the RailRoad range, which has a lower level of detail than the main range and in some cases uses older and

less detailed moulds to produce models more suited to the needs of the younger modeller.

It is now 95 years since Frank Hornby's first train set and ever since then the word Hornby has become synonymous with the model railway. Having grown from humble origins in Liverpool to having an international presence the company goes from strength to strength and will continue to provide to all the needs of modellers for many years to come. Ⓗ

Hornby's catalogues have evolved into comprehensive productions while the number of new products planned for each year has risen stratospherically.

17 New sound locomotives for 2016!

Twin Track Sound is taking pole position at Hornby for digital sound in 2016 with new steam and diesel locomotive sounds on the way.

Hornby is releasing an impressive line-up of 17 new sound fitted locomotives using its highly capable new Twin Track Sound (TTS) Digital Command Control (DCC) decoder – and 13 are with brand new sound files too!

Steam and diesel locomotives are in the lists, offering modellers a great choice of locomotives with the budget priced DCC sound decoder. On average TTS adds just £25 to the price of a model and each locomotive comes with a full set of running sounds together with up to 20 additional functions

Hornby's Twin Track Sound DCC decoder is to be fitted into a wider range of locomotives in 2016. Most will use a 28mm round speaker.

for each model including whistles/ horns, brakes and more. All sound functions can be controlled with a digital handset.

TTS is to become available in Hornby's top of the range models for the first time in 2016 - the 2014 launch of TTS being focused on the RailRoad product line. Returning in 2016 after their debuts in 2015 are new versions of the GWR 'King' 4-6-0 and LNER 'A4' 4-6-2 in the steam section together with the Class 40 and Class 47 in the diesel category – all with new liveries and identities to those released during the past year.

TWIN TRACK SOUND STEAM LOCOMOTIVES 2016

Class	Description	Period	Cat No.
GWR 'Castle' 4-6-0	5050 *Earl of St Germans*, BR lined green, early crests	1950s	R3383TTS
GWR 'King' 4-6-0	6006 *King George I*, BR lined green, late crests	1960s	R3384TTS
SR 'Schools' 4-4-0	30933 *King's Canterbury*, BR lined green, late crests	1950s/1960s	R3386TTS
SR 'Merchant Navy' 4-6-2	35023 *Holland Afrika Line*, BR lined green, early crests	1950s	R3382TTS
LMS '2P' 4-4-0	40626, BR lined black, early crests	1950s	R3459TTS
LMS '4F' 0-6-0	44918, BR black, late crests	1960s	R3460TTS
LMS 'Black Five' 4-6-0	45116, BR lined black, early crests	1950s	R3385TTS
LNER 'A4' 4-6-2 (RailRoad model)	4468 *Mallard*, LNER garter blue	1930s	R3395TTS
BR 'Britannia' 4-6-2	70001 *Lord Hurcomb*, BR lined green, early crests	1950s	R3387TTS
BR Crosti '9F' 2-10-0 (RailRoad model)	92025, BR black, early crests	1950s	R3396TTS

TWIN TRACK SOUND DIESEL LOCOMOTIVES 2016

Class	Description	Period	Cat No.
Class 20 (RailRoad model)	20163, BR blue	1970s-1990s	R3394TTS
Class 31	31239, BR blue	1970s/1980s	R3391TTS
Class 40 (RailRoad model)	40164, BR blue	1970s/1980s	R3392TTS
Class 43	43311 and 43312, Virgin East Coast livery	2015-2016	R3390TTS
Class 47 (RailRoad model)	47033, Railfreight sub-sector livery	1990s	R3393TTS
Class 60	60012, EW&S maroon and gold	2000s	R3389TTS
Class 67	67004 *Cairn Gorm*, Caledonian sleeper livery	2000s	R3388TTS

Most impressive is the list of new additions to the TTS roster. On the steam front these include the GWR 'Castle' 4-6-0, SR 'Schools' 4-4-0 and original condition 'Merchant Navy' 4-6-2, LMS '2P' 4-4-0, '4F' 0-6-0 and 'Black Five' 4-6-0 plus the BR 'Britannia' 4-6-2 and Crosti '9F' 2-10-0. This lifts the range of available steam sounds to 15 to include the 2014 released Peppercorn 'A1' 4-6-2, Gresley 'A3' 4-6-2, Gresley 'A4' 4-6-2 and 'P2' 2-8-2 and 2015 released Collett 'Hall' 4-6-0.

On the diesel front new sound files have been put together for the Class 20, 31, 43 (High Speed Train), 60 and 67, offering an attractive selection of eight TTS diesel sound decoders including the 2015 released Class 37, 40 and 47.

The new range of TTS locomotives are due to be released progressively through 2016. The full list of planned sound locomotives together with their identities above in Table 1 (steam) and Table 2 (diesel).

Visit *www.hornby.com* for more information. Ⓗ

● **See pages 98-99 for more on getting the most out of Hornby's diesel Twin Track Sound locomotives.**

17 new sound fitted locomotives are being released in 2016 using the Hornby Twin Track Sound decoder. One of the highlights is Class 67 67004 *Cairn Gorm* in Caledonian sleeper colours.

Twin Track Sound

Entering the digital sound market was once an expensive process, but not anymore with the arrival of Hornby's Twin Track Sound decoders. With an impressive list of new TTS locomotives planned for 2016 Paul Chetter explains how to get the best from the diesel range.

Hornby's entirely new Digital Command Control (DCC) sound decoder was designed from the ground up to produce the most realistic sounds and driver experience at a very attractive price.

A Twin Track Sound (TTS) equipped model typically costs around £25 more than the equivalent DCC ready model without any decoder fitted. This compares favourably with the £100 plus normally added as a premium for sound elsewhere for high end decoders.

The goal is to ensure that every new owner can operate the model successfully and with accurate sounds directly 'out of the box'. To satisfy the more experienced operator, and those developing their driving skills with TTS equipped locomotives, the automatic sound has been enhanced with control features for optional manual overrides plus the ability to adjust many useful parameters.

Each diesel-electric locomotive features sounds recorded from real examples. In order for you to judge how closely the TTS system can produce the sounds that real locomotives make, a basic understanding of how the real locomotives work is important.

Most British main line locomotives are driven by electric motors coupled to the driven axles. These are called traction motors. Some locomotives receive their power from an external source - overhead power lines or electrified third rails - while others have a diesel engine onboard which drives a generator to produce the required electrical power to operate the traction motors.

The diesel engine is not mechanically coupled to the wheels, so its sound is not directly linked to speed - in many circumstances there is a lag between the sound of increased power and any visual effect it has on speed or acceleration. Similarly, the diesel engine speed and power may be decreasing yet the train may continue at its current speed or even begin to accelerate.

In general, most sound decoders work on the assumption that higher speed requires more power so as the model travels faster, the engine sounds automatically increase. In reality, this is not accurate in many circumstances. Even in its fully automatic mode TTS will provide a more sophisticated representation than this.

Additionally, TTS decoders have inbuilt features rarely found on far more expensive alternatives that will dramatically improve the appropriateness of the sounds played.

Simulating reality

Imagine you are about to drive a real locomotive with a train of 1,000tons coupled to it. To set off

first you will sound the horn (Function key F2) to warn others that the train is about to move, release the brakes and feed in power with the control lever. Power needs to be built up steadily to avoid wheel slip or overstressing the traction motors.

To start a heavy train will require higher power from the engine to overcome inertia than if this were a light engine movement. The control lever would be moved to a higher power setting until inertia is overcome. Once the train is moving, you might need to reduce power to maintain a steady speed.

TTS decoders automatically provide the sound of brake release followed by an initial burst of power to move the train, followed by a power reduction once moving. By adjusting the way you add speed from your controller you can induce low, medium or high power bursts and determine whether the power subsequently drops and by how much.

Alternatively, an immediate 'full power' signal can be issued by engaging key F8 on a DCC handset. It only affects the engine sounds, the locomotive will not move until your throttle sends an acceleration command, and once engaged it will simulate a locomotive working at full capacity to move a heavy train or climb a gradient.

Normally, lower power will be required to maintain a given speed than for acceleration to that speed. The engine sound of a locomotive which has achieved its desired speed should reduce in its sound effects to reflect this correctly.

On the TTS decoders this has been provided a number of ways. Firstly by reducing the speed steps on a DCC handset by 1 will reduce the engine sounds to the next power band below with a barely noticeable impact on actual speed. Alternatively function key F6 will 'notch down' the engine sounds to the next power band

down without the need to change the speed setting at all. The third way of changing the engine speed without affecting the model's actual speed is to engage F7 which creates a larger drop in power to idle to allow a locomotive to coast, just as it would when the driver reduced power to travel down a gradient or to slow the train's progress on the approach to a station.

Gradient simulation

Your train is now travelling downhill. With 1,000tons pushing, the engine will probably not be applying power. To an outside observer, the engine will be idling but the train will be accelerating. The decoder must provide continuous idling sounds even when you increase speed steps to simulate the heavy load accelerating the train without input from the engine. TTS key F7 performs this task easily, without which it would be difficult to reproduce this effect. Consecutive

presses of F5 will each increase the power by one level allowing the model to go from coasting down grade to travelling on the level or even up a steep gradient on full power.

If you are running light engine in the yard and the speed limit is 5mph this can be replicated too. When the drive is engaged and the engine is running at idle, releasing the brakes will allow the locomotive to move without increasing power. TTS decoders automatically allow the locomotive to move without power ramping at low speed steps. For a higher speed movement without engine increasing power, just engage F7 before opening the throttle.

This seamless blend of automatic and manual interventions is so flexible in outcomes that all normal combinations of rail speed and engine power can be faithfully reproduced easily and, after a little practice, intuitively. ⊞

USEFUL LINKS

For the full range of new Twin Track Sound steam and diesel locomotives for 2016 see pages 96-97.

Twin Track Sound was introduced to Hornby's RailRoad diesel models in 2015. In 2016 TTS is coming to more of Hornby's range offering more great value DCC sound locomotives.

D232

LNER
'B12' 4-6-0

Many British railway companies turned to the
4-6-0 wheel arrangement in the early 20th
century and the Great Eastern Railway was
no exception with its long-lived 'B12'
class, which debuted in 1911.
Evan Green-Hughes reveals all.

In the early years of the 20th century the 4-4-0 was still the most popular design for express passenger work but in eastern England, as in other areas, the type had reached the maximum size that could be accommodated without increasing the axle weight beyond the track's limits. At this time the largest locomotives the Great Eastern Railway (GER) possessed were the famous 'Claud Hamilton' 4-4-0s but these were struggling with the increasing weight of trains on the main line from London to Colchester and Norwich and also with the boat trains running to Harwich Parkeston Quay.

The only solution was to build a locomotive with more axles to spread the weight, and in the GER's case this development was to see the introduction of the excellent 'S69' 4-6-0, later better known by its London North Eastern Railway (LNER) classification of 'B12'.

Lengthy gestation

Planning work on the new locomotive started in 1908 under the guidance of F V Russell, who was in charge of locomotive design at Stratford Works under Chief Mechanical Engineer S D Holden. Construction of the first example did not take place for three years due to pressure of other work. What emerged though was a 4-6-0. It was a compact engine which looked bigger than it actually was due to being fitted with an extremely large two window cab. Based on the general design of the 'Claud Hamilton' the 'B12' was fitted with a 5ft 1in diameter boiler which was the largest that could be accommodated within the loading gauge, and this fed two cylinders of 20in x 28in set in between the frames. Driving wheels were of 6ft 6in diameter, which was less than the 'Clauds', in order to lose some of the additional height gained by the use of the bigger boiler. As the GER used air brakes for its trains the 'B12' was fitted with air brake equipment. The general appearance was enhanced by the use of decorative valances over the driving wheels and the use of ornamental brass beading around the splashers above the wheels.

The locomotive was also designed with a very short wheelbase which assisted with its route availability. A very short tender was also supplied which contained 3,700 gallons of water and four tons of coal, with the complete engine and tender thus being able to be accommodated on all of the GER's standard 50ft turntables.

From the outset the 'B12s' proved very successful and further examples were ordered over following years. Stratford Works built 70 between 1911 and 1920 but as the works was heavily engaged in war work the next batch was put out to tender with Beardmore and Co of Glasgow being successful and building 20 locomotives which were eventually delivered in 1920-1921. A final batch of 10 was added in 1928 when the London and North Eastern Railway (LNER) found itself short of motive power and a decision was taken to order a tried and tested design as a short term solution. These were commissioned from Beyer, Peacock and Co of Manchester and differed slightly from the originals in that they were equipped with Lentz valve gear, the decorative framing over ☞

Resplendent in LNER lined apple green 'B12/3' 4-6-0 8510 climbs Belstead bank out of Ipswich with a Norwich-Liverpool Street express in 1937. The 'B12/3' sub class was created in 1932 with the fitting of new larger diameter boilers by the LNER. George Grigs/Rail Archive Stephenson.

LNER 'B12' STATISTICS (AS BUILT)

Designer:	S D Holden
Built:	1911-1928
Total in class:	80
Withdrawn:	1945-1961
Builders:	GER Stratford
	WM Beardmore and Co
	Beyer, Peacock and Co
Purpose:	Express passenger
Wheel arrangement:	4-6-0
Weight (locomotive):	63tons 0cwt
Weight (tender):	38tons 6cwt
Bogie wheel diameter:	3ft 3in
Driving wheel diameter:	6ft 6in
Wheelbase:	48ft 3in
Boiler:	5ft 1in
Boiler pressure:	180psi
Cylinders:	Two, inside, 20in x 28in
Tractive effort:	21,969lbs

the driving wheels was omitted and the sideplay feature of the rear driving axle was not fitted. Other changes included the use of deeper frames between the driving axle and cylinders and a reduction in the number of small tubes within the boiler. There was also an extended smokebox and a plain cast iron chimney was fitted. On this batch the tender water scoop was operated by hand, instead of by air as in earlier examples.

In service

When new the 'B12s' were put to work on the Great Eastern's services between London, Colchester and Norwich and were also to be found on boat trains to Parkeston Quay, duties which they continued to fulfil until replaced and supplemented by larger locomotives in the early 1920s. After the grouping they passed to the LNER which led to the class being seen further afield. The company experimentally tried some of them on the Leeds to Doncaster route but it was felt that they were not suitable for this work and so they were returned to the Great Eastern.

Tests then took place in 1926 with 8526 on the former Great North of Scotland lines and it was found that the locomotive was an ideal replacement for the elderly 4-4-0s that were in use on services between Aberdeen and Elgin. Consequently as newer and larger 'Sandringham' 4-6-0s

In an impressive display of power 'B12/3' 61571 leaves Ipswich tunnel with the 3.14pm Yarmouth South Town-Liverpool Street on May 22 1957. Ken Cook/Rail Archive Stephenson.

were placed in service during 1931 on the Great Eastern section a number of 'B12s' were transferred to Scotland where they were initially used on goods and fish trains but later on passenger duties also. Some were also loaned to Eastfield shed in summer for use on excursion trains to Oban. They were tried on some expresses, but were found lacking and consequently were returned to the eastern Highlands.

The Second World War saw the 'B12s' perform on some very heavy trains, with loads of 500tons or more being common and some were used on air braked American ambulance trains which saw

them travel extensively over South West England. Following the war and the arrival of more modern locomotives such as the Thompson 'B1' 4-6-0s the majority of the English based 'B12s' were allocated to Stratford where they were mainly used on the semi-fast Southend trains. A steady decline followed with the first withdrawal, 8534, taking place in June 1945.

At nationalisation in 1948, 72 of the original 80 locomotives survived to see service with British Railways but withdrawals continued at a steady pace with one of the first being prototype locomotive 8500 which was taken out of service only six months later. By this time many of the class were employed on duties between Norwich and Cromer. The Scottish engines soldiered on until 1954 when the last was withdrawn from service from Keith shed. The final example of the class was 61572 which was retained as something of a

With a mixed rake of ex-LMS carriages behind 'B12/3' 61533 leaves Bourne with the Yarmouth-Leicester through train on March 25 1950. Gordon Hepburn/Rail Archive Stephenson.

celebrity engine at Norwich and was often used on Yarmouth to March parcels trains as well as railtours. It was withdrawn in 1961 and has since been preserved.

Alterations
During their working life all of the 'B12s' were modified or rebuilt and those in service in the final days had many differences from the original build. The LNER

used the class for experimental work with feed water heating and to this end 8509 was fitted with Worthington-Simpson apparatus on the left-hand running plate during 1926. 50 of the class were fitted with the ungainly French ACFI feed water heating apparatus between 1927 and 1937. The idea was that waste heat would be used to pre-warm boiler water 👉

LNER 'B12' BATCHES AND NUMBERING

Date	Builder	GER no.	LNER 1924	LNER 1944	BR
1911-1912	GER Stratford	1500-1504	8500-8504	1500-1504	61500-61504
1913	GER Stratford	1505-1519	8505-8519	1505-1519	61505-61519
1914	GER Stratford	1520-1529	8520-8529	1520-1529	61520-61529
1914-1915	GER Stratford	1530-1535	8530-8535	1530-1535	61530-61535
1915-1917	GER Stratford	1536-1540	8536-8540	1536-1540	61536-61540
1920-1921	WM Beardmore	1541-1560	8541-8560	1541-1560	61541-61560
1920	GER Stratford	1561-1570	8561-8570	1561-1570	61561-61570
1928	Beyer, Peacock		8571-8580	1571-1580	61571-61580

Notes: 1506 written off in an accident in July 1913, so never carried subsequent numbers. Not all locomotives survived to take their British Railways numbers.

1915 built 'B12/1' 8532 climbs Brentwood bank with a down goods train in 1927. The locomotive, now part of LNER stock, retains its original decorative valances. F.R. Hebron/Rail Archive Stephenson.

Capturing the profile of the rebuilt locomotives with 5ft 6in diameter boilers, 61565 stands at Nottingham Victoria after arriving from Grantham in 1951. *Jim Hall/Rail Archive Stephenson.*

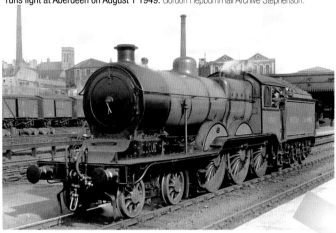

While the 'B12s' are best known for service on the Great Eastern section a number were allocated to Scotland following the arrival of new Gresley 'B17' 4-6-0s on the Great Eastern. 61513, carrying a hybrid LNER/BR apple green livery, runs light at Aberdeen on August 1 1949. *Gordon Hepburn/Rail Archive Stephenson.*

and this involved a small tank and pipework perched on the boiler top between the chimney and the dome. It wasn't very successful with any savings in fuel being offset by increased maintenance costs.

In 1926 8516 was fitted with Lentz oscillating poppet valve gear, being only the second such installation in the country to that date, and this resulted in an improvement in both performance and economy. 8525 was similarly fitted in 1928 and Lentz valve gear was then specified for the Beyer Peacock batch from new. However, subsequently major problems with the cam boxes, which were integral to the cylinders, caused Lentz equipped locomotives to be rebuilt from 1931 onwards with new long travel valves instead.

There were two major rebuilds for the 'B12s' during their lives. In 1932 8579 emerged from

Stratford fitted with an even larger boiler, this time of 5ft 6in diameter, and with a redesigned front end. The new boiler was similar to that fitted to the newer 'Sandringham' class and had the Gresley style round topped firebox. There were also modifications to the

valve gear and new long travel valves were fitted. This became the standard for all rebuilds and was known as the 'B12/3' and its adoption saw the disappearance of the ACFI apparatus and the Lentz valve gear from the class.

The rebuilt 'B12/3s' were

heavier than the original machines and as such were unsuited to work in Scotland and so, in 1943, the LNER embarked on a different modification to produce the 'B12/4'. In this variant a more modern boiler of 5ft 1in diameter was used in which the barrel was

'B12/1' 4-6-0 8568, fitted with an ACFI feed-water heater on its original smaller diameter boiler, passes Manningtree North Junction with an Ipswich-Liverpool Street slow in 1937. *George Grigs/Rail Archive Stephenson.*

'B12/3' 4-6-0s 8555 and 8509 arrive at Westerfield double heading a down slow in 1937. *George R. Grigs/Rail Archive Stephenson.*

'B12' SUB CLASSES

'B12/1'	GER locomotives with 5ft 1in boiler and Belpaire firebox
'B12/2'	GER locomotives with 5ft 1in boiler, Belpaire firebox and Lentz poppet valves
'B12/3'	1932 rebuilds with 5ft 6in diameter boiler and round topped firebox
'B12/4'	1943 rebuilds with 5ft 1in diameter boiler and round topped firebox for Scotland

rolled from a single plate and the tubes were arranged differently, cutting down on weight. These locomotives were around six tons lighter than the 'B12/3s' and nine were rebuilt in this way.

The 'B12s' were all equipped with the same type of tender but those working on the Midland and Great Northern and Great North of Scotland sections were fitted with tablet changing apparatus. Some of the Scottish allocation was given tenders from 'B17' 4-6-0s in their later years, the 'B17s' having been provided with larger LNER group standard tenders.

Sole survivor

Only one 'B12' made it into preservation. Following its period as a celebrity engine and mascot at Norwich 61572 was bought in working order by the Midland and Great Northern Joint Railway Society and in 1963 embarked on the 260-mile 'Wandering 1500' railtour. It then went into storage before being taken to the North

Norfolk Railway at Sheringham, along with 'J15' 0-6-0 65462. By then the locomotive was in poor condition.

In 1977 an appeal for its restoration commenced but the work was plagued with problems, including suppliers going out of business and delays in the supply of components. This was so much so that the locomotive was shipped out to Kloster Mansfeld near Leipzig in Germany where a traditional steam era workshop was still in existence. Unfortunately a change of management at that plant resulted in a dispute, by which time the locomotive was in pieces, and this meant that work was not completed until December 1994.

The sole-surviving 'B12' finally re-entered service in 1995 and commenced an illustrious career on the North Norfolk Railway, where it is considered to be the line's flagship engine. It has carried a number of liveries in its preservation career, including

LNER apple green, unlined black and BR black. It was out of service again for another rebuild between 2007 and 2012, since when it has appeared at a 'Steam on the Met' event and has made guest appearances at many other steam railways in the UK as well as being a regular performer at its home line in Norfolk.

Considering that the 'B12' design was so constricted by outside factors such as available turntable length, restricted axle loading and overall size the class turned out to be highly successful. Although only intended for services in East Anglia they proved themselves quite capable of working in the more severe terrain of the north of Scotland where they acquitted themselves well. It is a testament to their design that only eight of the class failed to make it into British Railways ownership and that today one survives to haul trains on one of our premier heritage railways. Ⓗ

Building a
Skaledale station

The station is at the heart of many railway systems. Mike Wild offers guidance for building a steam era station using Hornby's extensive Skaledale range as the basis.

TOOLS AND GLUES

- Contact adhesive
- Super glue
- Craft knife
- Tweezers
- Cutting mat
- Small scissors

A Maunsell 'King Arthur' approaches the station and passes the wood yard. All of the buildings are from the Skaledale collection, even down to the brick walls.

Creating a realistic station setting is so much more achievable with the extensive range of buildings and accessories in the Hornby Skaledale range. Ready built, painted and detailed buildings make it a straightforward process, but it still needs thought to plan out a project which will work.

The theme for our station – which uses the new High Brooms building collection as its inspiration - is a Southern Region through station with a bay platform to the front and a goods loop to the rear. There is a junction between the goods and fast line while at the rear is the compact locomotive servicing shed with the imposing South Eastern Railway style two-road shed as the main feature.

This station project uses a pair of 4ft x 2ft baseboards and has been designed more as a diorama than a working railway – that doesn't mean it can't be a working model as it is fully wired up and ready to run. Even though this is a static model for the time being, the methods and ideas can be employed on any railway layout, no matter what size.

The advantage of our 8ft long model is that it offers scope to introduce a substantial pair of platforms together with a small locomotive servicing area to

the rear. In addition to the High Brooms collection we've scoured the Skaledale range past and present to bring together a model with a realistic setting.

Additions include the ever useful platform sections, a water tower, coal stage, lamp huts, brick walling and a small selection of terrace houses – all finished in suitable red brick to give the whole scene a matching flavour.

The project started by simply mocking up the area with buildings and lengths of track. This soon showed up where items would and wouldn't work and led to a final trackplan to suit the area. Items were adjusted to suit and once

satisfied with the arrangement track was laid as per the feature on pages 38-43. With that completed the next phase was ballasting using the methods shown on pages 80-83 which led onto the enjoyable task of detailing.

The final phase is never ending. What we have achieved is a big step towards what could be deemed as a completed model, but there are always new accessories, details and features that can be built into a model.

The step by step guide shows how we went about creating this station scene highlighting important considerations and ideas for making your station even better. ☞

WHAT WE USED

Product	Cat No.
Pillar box	R8579
Telephone kiosk	R8580
Loading bay platform pack	R8584
Coal stage	R8587
Platform steps pack	R8604
Platform straights	R8614
Platform ramps	R8615
Terrace house (left-hand)	R8621
Footbridge	R8641
Platform lamps	R8673
Platform benches	R8674
Milk churns	R8678
Bicycles	R8679
Straight walls	R8744
Corner walls	R8745
Concrete platelayers hut	R9512
Great Northern Railway water tower	R9639
Weighbridge office	R9777
Lamp huts	R9783
Corrugated iron workshop	R9810
Platform signalbox	R9814
High Brooms station	R9818
High Brooms platform building	R9819
Engine shed	R9822
Station office	R9824
Railway stores	R9825

The compact engine shed is busy preparing a selection of Drummond designed locomotives.

STEP **BY** STEP — BUILDING A STATION WITH HORNBY SKALEDALE PRODUCTS

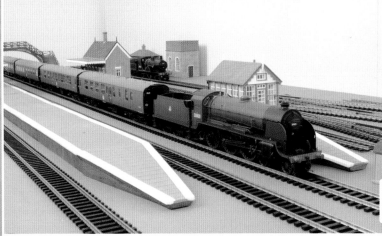

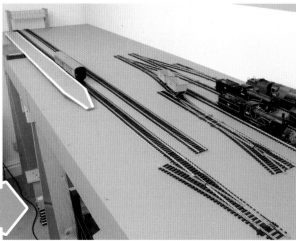

STEP 1
The project starts by laying out the main components on the baseboards. The full length of each platform was unboxed and positioned so that the track could be arranged to suit their positions.

STEP 2
With the general arrangement settled track laying followed using 1/16in thick cork with the track pinned on top as per the feature on pages 38-43.

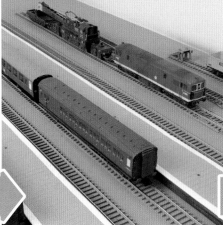

STEP 3
An important – and enjoyable phase – of every model project is testing. Having laid and wired the track a selection of different locomotives were run around the yard and through the station to check that everything worked and clearances to the platforms were acceptable.

STEP 4
The track was weathered next using Humbrol No. 29 from an aerosol – taking care to cover the point blades with masking tape before paint application. The platform sections were fixed in place with contact adhesive next and a selection of carriages were kept to hand to check that different vehicle types would clear the platform edges.

STEP 5
Ballasting of the track formation followed using diluted PVA wood glue as detailed in the ballasting feature on pages 80-83. This moves the layout up to the next level ready for the start of detailing.

A Drummond 'M7' 0-4-4T stands in the bay platform as a Bulleid 'West Country' 4-6-2 waits to depart on the main line.

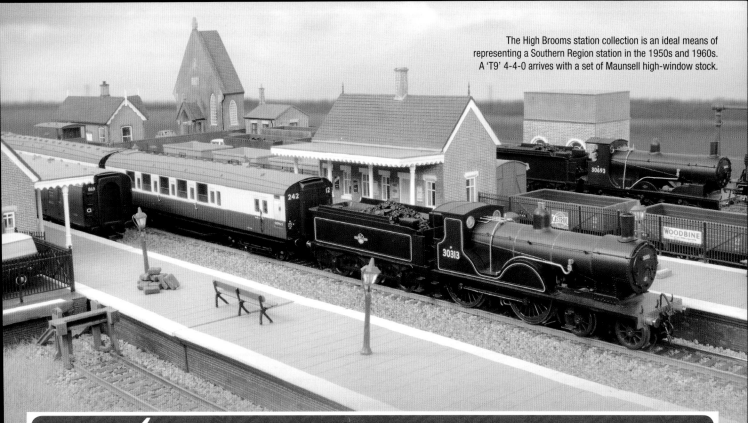

The High Brooms station collection is an ideal means of representing a Southern Region station in the 1950s and 1960s. A 'T9' 4-4-0 arrives with a set of Maunsell high-window stock.

STEP **BY** STEP — BUILDING A STATION WITH HORNBY SKALEDALE PRODUCTS

STEP 6

To assist in creating the theme for the layout red brick walling was added around the rear of the engine shed. The new space to the right will be used to add a row of terrace houses.

STEP 7

Walling was continued along the entire rear edge of the model to create an end point for the scenery.

STEP 8

A void between the edge of the track in the yard and the rear wall needed texture to finish it off. This was done by sprinkling chinchilla sand – a very fine sand available from pet shops – over the bare areas and fixing it in place by spraying it with a fine mist of water followed by application of diluted PVA glue (with a couple of drops of detergent added) applied with a syringe.

STEP 9

To detail the yard we found a set of three old Tri-ang-Hornby die-cast water cranes on a second-hand stall. At £4 with broken pipes they were a bargain. The old pipes were removed and replaced with heat shrink tubing of the right diameter to revive them.

The imposing new engine shed forms the backdrop to an 'S15' 4-6-0 passing a 'T9' 4-4-0 on the station approach.

STEP **BY** STEP / BUILDING A STATION WITH HORNBY SKALEDALE PRODUCTS

STEP 10

The area around the coal stage was detailed with a variety of grades of coal obtained from a local model shop. This was spread around the coal road to suggest a build up of dropped coal from filling tank engine bunkers and fixed in place with the same diluted PVA method as the chinchilla sand.

STEP 11

The chinchilla sand, while adding exactly the texture we wanted, was far from the right colour for a grubby steam era depot. To change its colour heavily diluted black paint was washed onto areas covered with the sand to tint it black. Multiple washes were applied for the final result.

STEP 12

To blend the ground texture into the rear wall static grasses from were added using a static grass puffer bottle. This type of grass texture adds great height and tone to model grasses.

STEP 13

Moving back to the station, and the first elements to be added were a telephone kiosk, post box together with fencing from a local model shop. This spear fencing is readily available from model shops in straight lengths and, as here, as gates. It is glued in place with small amounts of superglue.

STEP 14

Along the rear edge of the second platform spear fencing was added along the full length to separate the passenger side from the goods loop behind.

STEP 15

Station detailing continued with the addition of benches and lamps – both from the Skaledale collection.

STEP 16

Adding a touch of period character are these high quality printed signs from a specialist supplier. They are supplied on sheets and can be cut out with scissors and fixed in place with contact adhesive on the spear fencing.

STEP 17

Platform trolleys and luggage bring more life to the station together with features such as milk churns. These are all positioned loosely so that they can be moved to different locations should we wish to. If you decide to fix them down, small amounts of contact adhesive are ideal.

STEP 18

To finish off the foreground on the approach to the station the corrugated iron workshop was set inside a red brick wall to represent a timber yard. The timber features are from a pack by specialist supplier.

The front siding at the shed is ideal for displaying a crane or other rolling stock.

RailMaster is an intelligent software which features the ability to take control of a model railway through a computer. Locomotives, points, signals and other features can all be controlled at the click of a mouse.

Digital Command Control

New technology is transforming model railways. Mark Chivers looks at the exciting opportunities of 'going digital'.

Digital Command Control has brought new levels of operation to model railways including the ability to control lights and sounds on locomotives as well as their direction and speed of travel.

Digital Command Control (DCC) is an exciting and rewarding development of the hobby because it puts you in direct control of each locomotive on a layout as if you were in the cab yourself. Not only that - you can also control points and accessories as well as operate sound modules within the locomotive to emulate real sounds and much more.

Imagine, for a moment, that your DCC sound fitted diesel locomotive is ticking over at the head of a rake of carriages in the platform. A few function button presses and the sound of carriage doors slamming and a guard's whistle can be heard. Next, a few points change, the

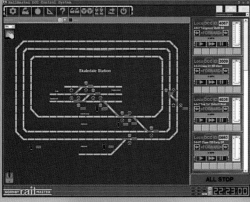

Track plans in RailMaster can be drawn to reflect the layout they control. This plan is for the Skaledale station which features on pages 106-111. Locomotive lists can be generated to suit specific fleets.

The design element of RailMaster allows complex track plans to be recreated quickly and simply. A series of pre-determined components is selected from the menus on the left and dropped into place on the grid to create the plan.

route is set and the colour light signal turns green. With a blast of the horn, power is applied, the locomotive brakes release, engine sounds increase and you're off. As the last carriage passes it, the colour light signal returns to red and your train continues on the next leg of its journey. This whole sequence is possible from one just controller – what fun!

How does it work?

Traditional analogue Direct Current (DC) controllers feed power to the track using a combination of voltage and polarity. As the voltage is increased to the track from the power controller the locomotive

moves faster and as voltage is decreased, the locomotive slows down. Direction is controlled by changing the polarity of the current delivered to the track. With DC, all locomotives on the same stretch of track will move when power is applied unless they occupy an electrically isolated section.

DCC works by feeding a constant voltage supply to the tracks so that it is always available to the locomotives. However, the locomotives will only move when a digital signal is transmitted through the running rails to a decoder fitted within a specific locomotive. This data is then translated into actions, such as moving forwards or turning

lights and sound functions on or off. A series of Configuration Variables (CVs) feature on each DCC decoder, containing a specific set of values. These CV values determine the running characteristics and operation of a locomotive or accessory, which can be read and fine-tuned using a suitable DCC controller.

DCC decoders are required for all locomotives and accessories on a digital layout. Each locomotive will require its own uniquely addressed locomotive decoder while turnouts and static accessories on a layout such as colour light signals, uncouplers or a motorised turntable require connection to an accessory decoder, which can typically be used for up to four accessories.

Why choose DCC?

DCC operation enables more than one locomotive to operate on the same stretch of track and in opposite directions if necessary. This added freedom to control the locomotive and not the track also opens up more possibilities for operating realistic shunting, freight and passenger trains. DCC also requires less and simpler wiring than traditional methods of control as many of the accessories and points can be operated from a single controller. By reducing the amount of wire required fewer wire connections are needed between baseboards, assembly of portable layouts a simpler task.

Hornby and DCC

Hornby's digital product range includes a three-tier range of DCC

TOP TIPS

1 Keep things simple and move one step at a time.

2 The Select, Elite and eLink have different abilities. Check their specifications before making your choice.

3 Always use a programming track when adjusting locomotive CVs.

4 Keep a record of each locomotives address and any CV changes which have been made for future reference.

5 Choose a simple locomotive as your first DCC installation project – diesel locomotives tend to be straightforward.

6 Set yourself attainable goals in upgrading a locomotive fleet to digital – doing it 'overnight' will be expensive.

7 Plan out an addressing system early and stick to it so that all addresses follow a set pattern.

8 When adding accessory decoders select number ranges for certain aspects, for example 1-10 for points and 20-29 for signals.

9 If you have a big layout consider keeping analogue control for one circuit and introducing DCC for another (but you must keep them separate).

10 Enjoy it! Digital control brings a whole new world of operation to model railways.

control systems or command stations, as they are more commonly known, which have developed significantly since the company first introduced them.

The Select DCC controller (Cat No. R8213) featuring a single rotary power throttle, numeric push button key pad and two-digit LCD display was the first of the company's new breed of DCC control unit to be developed. This was followed by the Elite DCC controller (R8214), boasting increased functionality, two rotary power throttles, larger LCD display and push buttons. The most significant recent development is Hornby RailMaster (R8144), a powerful software-based computer control DCC system. In addition, it has developed the eLink controller (R8312) which has the internal components of the Elite but has no physical controls - its purpose 👉

being to act as an interface between RailMaster and the layout.

Select

Hornby's Select DCC controller is an entry level system which is included within its digital train sets. The Select is more than just a basic controller though, as it is capable of addressing 59 different locomotives and 39 different points and accessories. The Select also enables addresses to be changed as well as the creation of double-headed trains and altering locomotive acceleration and deceleration rates. It can also operate up to 29 DCC sound functions on suitably equipped locomotives.

Supplied with a 1amp transformer, this provides enough power for up to three locomotives to be controlled at a time. A separate 4amp transformer is also available to supply additional power if required.

Hornby also produces a Select Walkabout DCC controller (R8235) which is identical to the regular Select unit but is supplied without a power transformer as the Walkabout receives its power from the main unit when connected. The Select Walkabout controller is designed to be linked to the standard Select through the Xpressnet RJ12 sockets at the rear of the control units and up to nine Walkabout units can be connected for finer control of individual locomotives.

Elite

The Hornby Elite DCC controller is the next level up from the Select and features twin rotary controllers

DCC TERMINOLOGY

Accessory decoder	Fixed location digital decoder that can control signals, point motors and other accessories
Address	Identifying number for a DCC fitted locomotive or accessory decoder
Command station	Control hub of a DCC operated layout
Consisting	Two or more locomotives operating together using the same DCC address
CVs	Configuration Variable. Programmable DCC decoder settings
DCC	Digital Command Control
DCC booster	Provides extra power rating to the track to improve DCC signals and allow more locomotives to be operated
DCC fitted	Model supplied with a factory fitted DCC decoder
DCC ready	Model supplied with a DCC decoder socket only and no decoder
Decoder	Printed circuit board for operating model railway locomotives and accessories
Function Output	Used to control functions and features on DCC fitted locomotive or carriages such as lights and sounds
Main track	DCC term for operational railway layout
Power bus	DCC layout power supply cable with dropper wires feeding the track at regular intervals
Programming track	DCC term for track which is separate from the main line for programming locomotive CVs
Route setting	Series of points operating together to form a defined route on a layout
Speed steps	DCC power control increments. The more steps you have, the smoother the speed transition. Equally divided into 14, 28 and 128 steps depending on controller setting.

with press switch functionality together with a 17 button keyboard. Locomotives can be controlled using the two rotary throttles while a system of step-by-step routines is followed depending on the task required such as changing or reading individual CV values by simply pressing the menu button on the controller and scrolling through options using one of the rotary controls. To select a menu item, you push the rotary control until it clicks and repeat the process for the next

step and so on. An easy-to-follow instruction manual is included for the main routines required.

Up to ten locomotives can be controlled at the same time using the supplied 4amp transformer and the Elite can also address and store up to 254 locomotive addresses and 255 accessory addresses.

Whilst the Select operates using two-digit addresses, the Elite system can call upon two or four-figure addresses from 0-9999 and can also store names for specific

locomotives too. This feature rich system also includes a choice of programming modes, scale clock setting and it supports Railcom - a sophisticated feedback system - which Hornby utilises through its Sapphire DCC decoder (R8245) for aspects of its operation.

The Elite can also operate up to 29 DCC functions on locomotives such as turning directional or cab lights on/off as well as sound functions including warning horns/whistles, brake noises, shunting sounds and much more on DCC sound-fitted models.

Another advantage of the Elite controller is its USB socket at the rear which means it can be easily connected to a computer for operation of a layout using suitable compatible software. It also allows the Elite's firmware to be updated from time to time ensuring the controller is always operating at its optimum. Up to eight additional Hornby Select Walkabout DCC controllers can also be linked to the Elite using the Xpressnet RJ12 sockets at the rear of the units for extra control options. A large red emergency stop button is also provided if things get out of hand.

RailMaster

Hornby's impressive RailMaster computer software launched in 2011 and is suitable for use with most Windows PCs. The system is designed for easy operation in conventional computer click mode with a mouse or it can be configured for touch-screen use and used in conjunction with a Hornby Elite controller linking between the PC

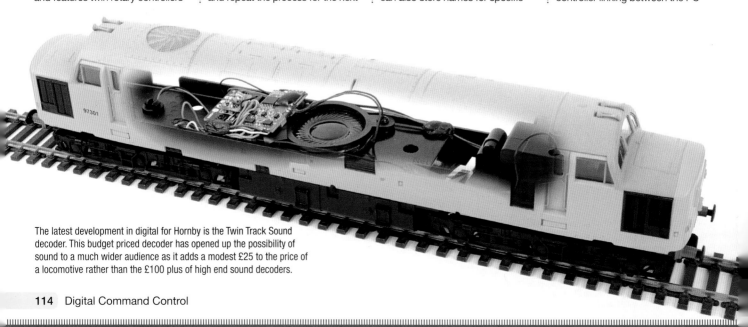

The latest development in digital for Hornby is the Twin Track Sound decoder. This budget priced decoder has opened up the possibility of sound to a much wider audience as it adds a modest £25 to the price of a locomotive rather than the £100 plus of high end sound decoders.

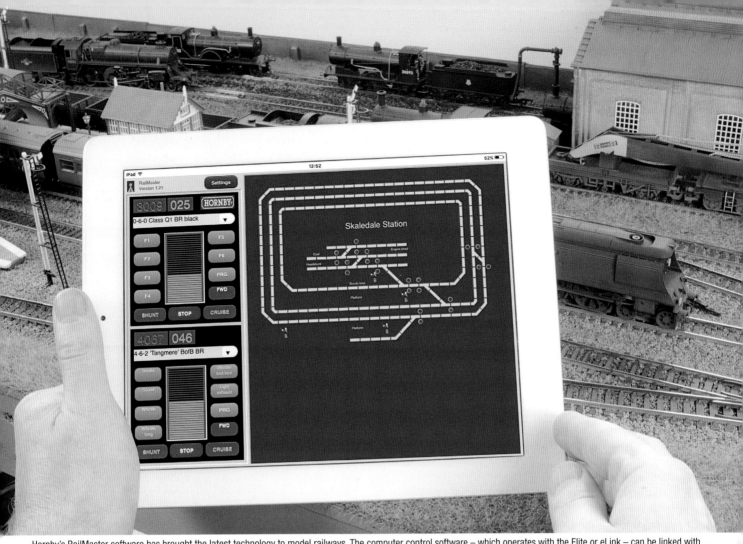

Hornby's RailMaster software has brought the latest technology to model railways. The computer control software – which operates with the Elite or eLink – can be linked with tablets and smart phones for even greater flexibility.

and the layout or Hornby's eLink computer interface (R8312), which replaces the Elite between the layout and the PC, but still offers the same functionality for RailMaster.

It is an incredibly powerful programme, bringing layout design and control together, enabling operation of an entire DCC layout from the PC screen as well as the ability to draw operational track plans of your layout with Hornby's range of operating accessories included, such as point motors, signals, motorised turntable and more, all of which can be controlled on screen.

Ease of use has been considered throughout and a database of over 2,500 profiled Hornby locomotives is included, each with built-in scale speeds included to make the task of assigning addresses that bit simpler. Each profile features a photograph of the locomotive and covers Hornby releases from the past 40 years. The process of adding your own additional locomotives is quick and simple and you can also upload your own photographs for inclusion

The Elite is Hornby's top end DCC controller which features twin control dials, a key pad and numerous functions. One connection from the back can be linked to multiple tracks.

in the database too.

RailMaster enables up to 9,999 individual locomotive addresses to be assigned and can also operate up to 2,048 points and accessories. Up to 25 DCC sound and light functions can be accessed on each locomotive while route setting is also possible, allowing you to set multiple points to change at the same time, thus creating a single route for your train. A second Hornby Elite or eLink can be connected to RailMaster to provide a separate dedicated power supply for points and accessories, if required.

In addition to showing one large main power controller on screen, the system also lets you hold a selection of smaller locomotive controllers on-screen together with the option to scroll through others offering plenty of flexibility and operation of a large number of locomotives simultaneously, provided you have the room of course!

Another clever option is the ability to create automated sequences,

which is particularly useful if you would like to run a shuttle train service separately to normal train operation. This automated sequence is time-based and enables the train to be moved as well as points changed, sound and light functions selected and pauses between movements, if necessary. For some real fun, why not insert one of the supplied pre-recorded station announcements as the train arrives in the platform?

The RailMaster system is ever evolving and the current optional pro-pack add-on offers extra functionality including a second large on-screen power controller, voice control of all movements using a microphone-enabled headset as well as the option to control multiple aspect signalling with automatic switching of other signals in sequence. It also caters for more specialised turnouts such as double slips and three way points and also provides new 45degree point elements in design mode to enable more complex track plans to be drawn. Printing of CVs, track ☞

plans and automated programme schedules are also possible.

RailMaster can also be operated on a range of smartphones and tablets by simply downloading the dedicated app and linking your device to your computer network, enabling true remote operation of the layout.

Locomotive decoders

With most Hornby 'OO' gauge locomotives available DCC ready and featuring decoder sockets for simple plug and play operation, preparing models for use is relatively straightforward – some models are also available DCC fitted, with decoders already factory-installed.

The majority of locomotives feature 8-pin decoder sockets as standard while a selection of the high-end DCC sound-fitted models include 21-pin DCC decoder sockets to take full advantage of the technology. Some smaller locomotives in the range such as the Sentinel industrial diesel shunters are fitted with specialised 4-pin sockets due to the limited space available.

To cater for these different socket types, Hornby produces suitable DCC decoders including a standard four function 8-pin decoder (R8249) with access to a limited number of CVs and its premium 21-pin Sapphire decoder (R8245) which features four functions, a 21-pin to 8-pin adaptor harness, low speed gearing, access to all CVs and some neat bespoke features including the ability to set the locomotive burn rate for fuel and water consumption and an option to set an automatic time-based shuttle sequence in operation using

The Select DCC controller is the introductory system from Hornby. Connecting it to the track is a simple process involving just two wires.

Railcom. A four-pin DCC decoder (X9659) is also available and is similar to the R8249 but fitted with a 4-pin socket for use with the Sentinel industrial diesel shunter.

Hornby's most recent addition to the decoder range is its in-house designed Twin Track Sound decoder designed to provide sounds at a low cost over the price of a standard Hornby Railroad/main range model. Typically, the decoders feature 18-26 functions depending on the locomotive type and include a broad selection of different sound files.

At the top end of the decoder spectrum is the ESU Loksound 21-pin DCC sound decoder which has been fitted to many of Hornby's main range locomotives in recent years. These impressive decoders have featured in both steam and diesel locomotives such as the Stanier 'Black Five' 4-6-0, Bulleid

'Merchant Navy' 4-6-2, Class 50 and Class 56 diesel locomotives.

All decoders are supplied with a default address of 0003, which can be changed using a DCC controller to something more appropriate for your control system. Numbering systems are a personal choice, but you may choose to use the last two digits of the locomotive number or even the first two followed by the last two digits of the number. Whatever system you choose remember to be consistent - otherwise there will come a time when you can't remember what address you gave a locomotive which could become frustrating.

For more on decoder specifications, see pages 60-63.

Accessories

Hornby's range of DCC accessories includes an accessory decoder (R8247) suitable for

controlling the operation of points, signals or motorised accessories with up to four items controlled using one decoder. A single pulse for solenoid point motors or a longer burst of power for accessories such as a motorised turntable can be programmed.

A DCC power and signal booster (R8239) is also available and is designed for use on particularly large or complex layouts where the DCC signal may suffer from deterioration due to the long distances involved and the number of locomotives in use. In such circumstances, additional power sections can be installed on the layout using the DCC power and signal booster and linked to the layout power feed to improve electrical and signal communication.

If you have a reverse loop where a single track feeds back on itself

Trains, track, signals, sounds, lights and more all come under the control of a single handset with DCC. Both of these locomotives - despite being on separate tracks - are controlled by one controller, the decoder inside each model receiving signals to instruct it on what to do next.

The eLink has been designed to work hand in hand with RailMaster software. It is an electronic box which has all the same functionally as the Elite, but without the key pad and buttons. Their place is taken by a computer.

in a balloon loop, for example, Hornby offers a useful reverse loop module (R8238) which is simple to install and does all the hard work for you, eliminating the potential electrical issues these track layouts can cause.

Finally, Hornby's simple but effective packs of digital electrical point clips (R8232) allow insulated frog points to be converted to 'live' points which then allows otherwise dormant locomotives to be on standby as power is then fed to all tracks irrespective of which direction the points are set. This is particularly useful if you have DCC sound locomotives as they will be able to tick over in sidings or station platforms ready for their next duty. Two clips are used per insulated frog point and simply clip in between the point blade and rail just ahead of the 'vee'. These clips are reversible if necessary and can be easily removed - plus they allow you to use existing points, which is ideal if you are on a limited modelling budget.

That's entertainment!

DCC certainly offers plenty of play value with an ever increasing range of DCC sound fitted locomotives available together with an extensive list of accessories.

Constant power to the track also helps to improve reliability of mechanisms and enables elements such as coach lighting to remain lit. In no time at all you'll discover the benefits of tinkering with CV values to improve the acceleration and deceleration characteristics of a locomotive and creating exciting track diagrams with operating points and signals.

Hornby's digital range is designed to be simple to set up, easy to use and, most importantly, fun to operate. ⬚

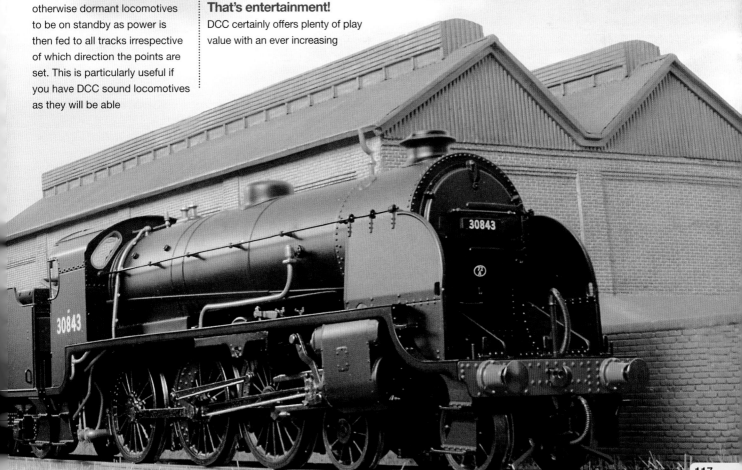

Granite station building, R9836.

SKALEDALE

2016

More than 25 new buildings are set to join the Skaledale collection in 2016 with railway and town themes.

Skaledale has become an essential part of the Hornby range with its collection of high quality cast resin buildings which come pre-painted, assembled and ready to place on a model railway.

Each year a new collection of buildings is released to add to the already extensive range of standard items. This year is no exception with 27 new items planned for 2016 covering railway and non-railway buildings.

A useful range of granite buildings based on the Settle and Carlisle style, is to be released on the railway front. Finished with green doors, gutters and downpipes this attractive collection will have plenty of potential for use across the regions. In the listings are a station building, waiting room, signalbox, engine shed and goods shed. Other railway highlights include a raised water tank.

Southern Region modellers - especially those with a leaning towards the South Eastern Railway routes through Kent - will be delighted with the addition of a model of Wateringbury signalbox, which still stands at the station even though it is no longer in use.

For those looking to extend their town scenes away from the railway, Skaledale will feature a new selection of eight town buildings together with a memorial, modern terrace house, a modern bungalow and useful additions such as a detached single garage and a triple garage too.

Visit *www.hornby.com* for full details of the 2016 Skaledale range. Ⓗ

Florist, R9831.

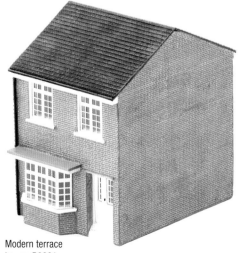

Modern terrace house, R9801.

Bakers shop, R9828.

Granite goods shed, R9841.

Granite waiting room, R9837.

Corner public house, R9833.

Timber signalbox, R9838.

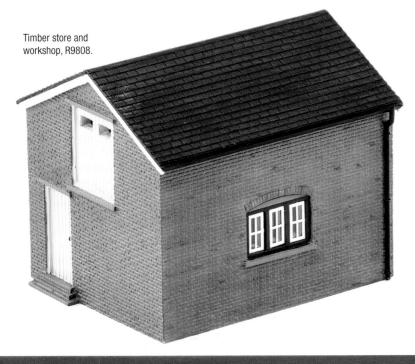

Timber store and workshop, R9808.

SKALEDALE BUILDINGS 2016

Description	Cat No.
Bakers shop	R9828
Toy shop	R9829
Shoe shop	R9830
Florist	R9831
Restaurant	R9832
Corner public house	R9833
Village tea rooms	R9834
Hardware store	R9835
Memorial	R9827
Detached brick garage	R9826
Modern terrace house	R9801
Modern prefabricated building	R9802
Tin house	R9803
Modern bungalow	R9807
Timber store and workshop	R9808
Shiplap lean-to	R9811
Triple garage	R9812
Ex-barrack rooms	R9813
Covered loading bay	R9815
Wateringbury signalbox	R9816
Raised water tank	R9817
Granite station building	R9836
Granite waiting room	R9837
Timber signalbox	R9838
Granite water tower	R9839
Granite engine shed	R9840

Peckett
'W4' 0-4-0ST

EVAN GREEN-HUGHES charts the history of an important design that while overlooked by many enthusiasts helped keep the wheels of industry turning for many decades.

Although much is known about locomotives built in the major works for the main line companies the same is not true of the thousands of small privately owned locomotives that used to work in factories, docks and sidings, including the 'W4' 0-4-0ST built by Peckett and Sons of Bristol. New to Hornby's 2016 range this follows a general increase in interest in modelling industrial railway systems in 'OO' scale.

In the days before the widespread use of road transport most large factories had their own internal railway systems, as did steelworks,

Peckett 0-4-0STs were employed across the country for industrial work. In the late 1950s a Peckett shunts a short set of wagons at Shap Granite Co. Gordon Edgar.

collieries, docks and municipal undertakings. Trains were worked into and out of these sidings by the main line railway companies but all internal movements were carried out by the companies themselves.

Several companies had lucrative businesses supplying the necessary motive power including Peckett, the Yorkshire Engine Company, Hunslet of Leeds, Hawthorn Leslie and the Vulcan Foundry. Production of steam engines was a major part of this business and some continued for a few years after British Railways itself chose to abandon steam in favour of diesel.

Peckett and Sons was established at the Atlas Engine Works in St George, Bristol, in 1880 having taken over the already established business of Fox, Walker and Company. It quickly established a range of simple and easy to maintain locomotives which shared many major components with each other. Peckett described its core market as "Collieries, Ironworks, Contractors, Tinplate Works, etc" but in reality there were few industries which did not take one of its engines. Four and six wheeled saddle tank engines were available and the company also built

stationary steam engines and in its earlier incarnation had been one of the few companies to produce the traction units for steam trams. Although much of the company's production was for the home market there were some locomotives built for export with the largest being an 0-8-0T for the Christmas Island Phosphate Company in 1931.

The works had a substantial order book throughout the latter part of the 19th century and the first half of the 20th and was particularly busy in the First and Second World Wars. Peckett locomotives were subject to a gradual improvement process ☞

rather than a series of radical revamps so they were never at the forefront of development and by the 1950s they were dated and unable to compete with the latest designs from other manufacturers or indeed with diesels. The company decided to produce its own diesel designs and consequently built a few diesel mechanical shunters, starting in 1956, but these were not particularly successful. Production of steam locomotives ceased in 1958 and the company went into decline, being taken over in 1961 by Reed Cranes and subsequently going out of business altogether.

The 'W' series

Peckett had turned out its first engine in December 1884, a small 0-4-0T with outside cylinders and side tanks built for the Cyfarthfa Ironworks of Merthyr Tydfil as No. 9, while the first of the famous saddle tanks was built the following year for Daniel Edwards contractors. The final steam engine was an 0-6-0T built in June 1958 for the Sena Sugar Estates in Portuguese East Africa, a 3ft gauge railway that already had several of Peckett's products.

Engines made by Peckett were well known for their fine workmanship and finish and made generous use of copper and brasswork and consequently many of them were very long lived. The 'W' class came in six basic variations ranging from the 'W2' of 1884 to the 'W7' of 1937 but amongst the six versions there were hundreds of detail differences because the company was very good at providing the exact

The famous Manchester Ship Canal made use of Peckett's fine locomotives. 1897 built No. 11 awaits its next movement on the system. *Hornby Archive.*

locomotive its customers wanted.

The basic 'W4' was a simple two-cylinder machine with a wheel diameter of 2ft 4in, having 'H' section wheel spokes and spring balanced safety valves, at least until about 1912 when a change was made to the later 'pop' type. A saddle tank was fitted above the boiler, leaving space underneath from which access could be obtained between the frames for maintenance without the need for an inspection pit. At the rear of the main frames the standard cab had cutout side sheets, a full spectacle plate and a full length roof but at the rear the sheeting only covered the bottom half of the cab.

A total of 140 examples were built of this design and many of them made the journey to their new homes under their own steam, starting their trip on the company's one mile long private branch line, a facility that at one time also served a number of local collieries.

Some of those built were supplied with cut down features, such as lower cabs and chimneys, while

there were also examples with shorter and lower saddle tanks. Full length rear cab sheets were fitted to many locomotives and buyers could specify a number of other fittings, such as toolboxes, steps, bunker design and handrails. However the firm was not keen on altering the basics of its engines at customer's request, considering that if the proven and successful design was not adequate for requirements then the company was not interested in the business.

Despite this there were one or two oddities, one of which was Pioneer, works number 484 of 1889, which was built for Nevill, Druce and Co of Llanelli for use in its copper works. Although still classed as a 'W4' this machine was equipped with two 14in x 18in inside cylinders but was otherwise very similar to all the others in the class. Works number 599 of 1895 for C Rowlands of Swansea had a rather odd arrangement of side sheets covering the motion as it was intended that it should travel over lines laid into the public road for part of its duties.

Presumably for the same reason the cab was largely open.

Main line operators

Although most of these engines served out their lives in the obscurity of industrial locations some did come into the ownership of the main line companies. In 1919 the Glasgow & South Western Railway took over Ayr harbour and with the deal came one steam engine, Peckett 'W4', works no 977. This was repainted and entered the railway's stock as 735 and after grouping was taken over by the London Midland & Scottish Railway and became 16043, serving for a time at Kilmarnock works and later at the Gleneagles Hotel branch. It was scrapped at Ayr in 1930.

Four more 'W4s' were purchased by C Rowlands for work at Swansea Harbour and they passed into the ownership of the Great Western Railway at the grouping of 1923, the two examples built in 1899 becoming 886 and 926 respectively, one built in 1902 becoming 930 and the final one which was built in 1904 becoming 933. The first three were withdrawn and scrapped in 1928/1929 but the last one was sold

While the 'W4' specification laid down the basics customers could request modifications to suit specific purposes. 1084 was the last 'W4' to be built in February 1906 and it featured a cut down cab, water tank and chimney to suit the Skinningrove Iron Co in Carlin How, Yorkshire. *Hornby Archive.*

Industrial railways meant locomotives worked in harsh conditions. Peckett 'W4' 0-4-0ST 851 raises steam on shed at Harworth Colliery in 1956. *Hornby Archive.*

off for further use in a colliery after which not much is known about it.

Works numbers 979/985, which were built for the Co-operative Wholesale Society in 1904-1905, were employed on the soap works branch at Irlam near Manchester where in addition to working the usual goods trains also found employment on the twice-daily workers passenger service from Irlam station into the works. For this an ex-Midland Railway six-wheel carriage was used and this survived long enough to become an exhibit at York Railway Museum.

Into preservation

Due to their extremely sound design and robust workmanship many of the 'W4s' had long lives despite being used in very harsh conditions, and consequently three of them survived long enough to be preserved. The example at the Sittingbourne and Kemsley Light Railway is of particular interest as it is the oldest surviving Peckett in the country, having been built in 1896. It was sent new to James Dunlop and Co's Clyde ironworks at Rutherglen where it was known as Bear. It remained on this site

for almost 50 years until when, in 1941, it required heavy repairs and was despatched to Andrew Barclay at Kilmarnock. After a rebuild it emerged as Mossend Engineering Works No 3 for work at that site and then put in a further 25 years' work before being taken out of service and passing into preservation. Currently it is on static display on an isolated piece of track.

The Foxfield Railway has 933 *Henry Cort* which was one of a pair delivered to the Ebbw Vale Steelworks in 1903. This served for

51 years before moving on to the same owner's ironstone quarries at Blisworth. After another three years it went to Irthlingborough Quarries where it worked until 1965 before moving to Foxfield and working the first trains there. It is currently awaiting repairs.

Daphne is an 1899 example built for the Tytherington Stone Company in Gloucestershire which ended its life in a playground on the seafront at Lytham. It passed into preservation at the Ribble Steam Railway in 2002 but has

considerable damage to its boiler and is also a static exhibit.

Enthusiasts traditionally had little interest in industrial steam yet there were hundreds of small locomotives such as the 'W4s' working away every day helping Britain to retain its position as a world economic leader. Peckett's products worked away largely unseen and unnoticed for many years and it is fitting that now they are beginning to attract the sort of attention that they richly deserve. Ⓗ

Peckett 'W4' 883 stands in the yard of the Lilleshall Company at Priorslee Ironworks in Shropshire. *Hornby Archive.*

![HORNBY]

Hornby's
INCREDIBLE
YEAR

Each year Hornby sets out to deliver an impressive range of locomotives, carriages and wagons, but 2015 was better than ever with **SEVEN** brand new steam locomotives reaching the shops along with carriages, wagons and more.
Mark Chivers looks back on the year past.

2015 was an exciting and busy year for Hornby with seven new locomotives covering Western, Southern and Eastern Region designs from the 'Big Four' and constituents, as well as BR designs, two new sets of carriages and two new wagons released in the past 12 months.

But it wasn't just new models that appeared during the year as a steady stream of models from previous years arrived with new running numbers and new liveries. Highlights included the Great Western Railway (GWR) 2-8-0Ts and 2-8-2Ts, a return for the Southern Railway (SR) 'King Arthur' 4-6-0 plus an array of diesels covering classes 31,

50, 56, 67 and more. In addition, a selection of exclusive models produced for Hornby's Collectors Club also appeared during the year, with more to come.

The popular Sentinel 0-4-0 diesel shunter reappeared in a new guise with outside coupling rods, plus the eagerly awaited diesel versions of the Twin Track Sound Digital Command Control (DCC) fitted locomotives appeared including a Class 37, 40 and 47.

Steam is king

For the new releases steam motive power was the main focus of the year. During the past 12 months production has caught up, seeing all the outstanding models from the 2014 range arrive together

with two of those announced in December 2015 at the catalogue launch. The final two from 2015 are close to release too.

The selection of new locomotive arrivals was impressive ranging from the diminutive Worsdell 'J15' 0-6-0 for the Great Eastern Region right through to the mighty GWR 'King' 4-6-0 and the equally attractive – although for very different reasons – Crosti-boilered BR '9F' 2-10-0.

The year started with the arrival of the Peppercorn 'K1' 2-6-0 – a model announced in the 2014 range. The first version, 62024, touched down in the final weeks of December 2014 in limited numbers with the full supply of this and two further versions – 62015

and 62027 – landing too. While the 'K1' was built to an LNER design, the first didn't enter traffic until 1949 and all were delivered in BR lined black livery. Hornby's model catered for both early and late crest styles offering modellers of the Eastern, North Eastern and Scottish Regions a suitable mixed traffic engine to head up all manner of duties from passenger to parcels and goods.

Covering territory at the opposite end of the country January 2015 also heralded the arrival of the new 'OO' gauge Great Western Railway (GWR) 'Hall' 4-6-0s in both the main and RailRoad ranges. 259 of these versatile locomotives were turned out from the GWR's Swindon

New all-steel K-type Pullman cars arrived in June 2015 with five versions being produced.

New to the goods wagons range in January 2015 was the 21ton hopper…

… together with the Derby built LMS horsebox.

An impressive range of much requested locomotives have debuted in the Hornby range in 2015. From left to right are the Drummond '700' 0-6-0, LNER 'D16/3' 4-4-0, Collett 'King' 4-6-0, Peppercorn 'K1' 2-6-0 and Crosti '9F' 2-10-0.

Works between 1928 and 1943 with Hornby's new version being supplied in both GWR and BR liveries. A special train pack containing former main line registered 'Hall' 4953 *Pitchford Hall* was issued containing three Mk 1 carriages and the 4-6-0 and titled the 'Tyseley Connection' while *Harry Potter* fans had the chance to own a brand new version of 5972 *Olton Hall* in its fictional maroon livery from the popular film franchise.

The charming 'J15' 0-6-0 was next to arrive when three versions touched down in February 2015 covering LNER, early BR and late BR black liveries. All three had detail variations including cab design, fitment of a Westinghouse air-pump to one version and a locomotive brake only model.

To provide adequate weight for this model the body is die-cast metal, but detail was still top of the priority list and included plenty of fine fittings.

A big surprise for many in the 2014 range was the announcement of the Drummond '700' 0-6-0 reflecting Hornby's move into producing useful smaller locomotives. The first of these fine freight engines arrived during June offering the Southern Region an important prototype which could sit side by side with such well received offerings as Hornby's 'M7' 0-4-4T, 'T9' 4-4-0 and 'N15' 4-6-0.

Introduced in 1897, 30 of these diminutive locomotives were 👉

HORNBY 2015 COLLECTORS CLUB EXCLUSIVES

Cat No.	Model	Livery
R3091	Hornby Club 0-4-0T 2012 60 *Queen Elizabeth II*	Plum
R3213	Hornby Club 0-4-0T 2013 3102	SR green
R3247	Stroudley 'A1X' 0-6-0 650 *Whitechapel*	Stroudley improved engine green
R3248	Stroudley 'A1X' 0-6-0 10 *Sutton*	KESR lined green
R3249	'Battle of Britain' 4-6-2 34070 *Manston*	BR lined green, early crests
R3250	LNER 'A3' 4-6-2 *Flying Scotsman*	LNER lined apple green
R3292	Hornby Club 0-4-0ST 2014 56011	BR lined black, early crests

built by Dubs and Co of Glasgow. The Hornby model reflected the class after rebuilding, which started in 1921, with a longer smokebox and raised boiler pitch.

Few locomotives have such a distinctive appearance as the Crosti-boilered BR '9F' 2-10-0s and a welcome and unexpected announcement in 2014 was this strangely popular class of 10. Crews loathed these engines for their abilities to fill the cab with smoke and soot, but enthusiasts marvelled at their side exhaust and unusual boiler arrangement.

Hornby's Crosti was placed in the RailRoad range and saw a brand new body tooling produced to represent the class – 92020-92029 – in both as built and modified form with a smoke deflector added. First off the new tools were 92027 in BR black with late crests without a smoke deflector and 92023 in BR black with late crests and a smoke deflector offering a wonderful heavy freight addition to the growing RailRoad collection.

Autumn triumphs

The first of the 2015 catalogue range to arrive was the Maunsell 'S15' 4-6-0 in October – a design which went back to the London and South Western Railway in 1920. Introduced by Robert Urie 45 were built – 20 to Urie's original design and 25 to the Southern Railway's modified Maunsell design with superheating.

Designed primarily for freight work the last of the class remained in service until the end of 1965 and seven have been preserved – two Urie and three Maunsell locomotives.

Hornby's model represents the Maunsell designed locomotives and three were released initially covering Southern Railway and BR liveries. The 'S15' also included a new tender in a straight sided bogie design released with 30843 – the other two featuring flared top bogie tenders matching that created for the Maunsell 'King Arthur'.

The autumn continued to be a busy period for Hornby with two more significant new arrivals

The latest arrival with Hornby's retailers is the mighty GWR 'King' 4-6-0. One of four versions in the model's debut year is 6029 *King Edward VIII* in BR lined green.

The humble Worsdell 'J15' 0-6-0 is a superb addition to the range and fills a gap in the market for much needed Great Eastern Region motive power alongside the 'D16/3'.

Hornby's ability to reproduce the Southern Region's attractive range of Maunsell designed locomotives is well known and its latest is the 'S15' 4-6-0 which arrived in October.

touching down during October and November. First out was the sublime LNER 'D16/3' 4-4-0 which was a welcome addition alongside the 'J15' 0-6-0 for the Great Eastern Region. This new 4-4-0 featured a die-cast boiler which meant that with clever chassis design no traction tyres were needed to give this model ample power to handle the trains it should. Four models arrived in the debut set covering LNER, British Railways and BR liveries with the addition of a weathered version with early BR crests.

With the year-end approaching, Hornby's GWR 'King' 4-6-0 arrived in November. Built at Swindon Works between 1927 and 1936, this impressive class of locomotives numbered 30 with the final locomotives remaining in traffic until withdrawal in 1962.

The GWR 'King' has long been a fixture of the Hornby catalogue – it produced its first in 1978 - and so it is only natural that this model should be developed further incorporating a greater amount of detail and the latest technology, which now includes a Twin Track Sound (TTS) fitted version. All of

the first batch were arriving in the shops in late November, giving rise to a new impetus to model the Great Western Railway and BR's Western Region and its fine collection of 4-6-0s.

All of the new steam locomotives released during 2015 came with an 8-pin Digital Command Control decoder socket. Apart from the Crosti '9F' – which had a locomotive mounted decoder socket – all featured a socket in the tender with the majority also having provision for installation of a 28mm round speaker too. Performance was improved too, with a new motor/mechanism design in the 'J15' and 'S15' taking the quality of running characteristics to a new level.

Carriage and wagon
Of course the Hornby range isn't just about locomotives and the carriage and wagon sections have benefitted greatly in 2015 from new releases.

Quick off the block was the first item of new 'OO' gauge rolling stock from the 2015 range - the BR 21ton steel hopper wagon. Announced just a few weeks

earlier as part of the Hornby 2015 catalogue range, the first models arrived during January.

More than 20,000 of this prolific wagon type were built through the years, Hornby's model representing a London and North Eastern Railway (LNER) design from the post nationalisation period in the early 1950s.

Also delivered in January was the London Midland & Scottish Railway (LMS) horse box. Built at the LMS' Derby Works in the 1930s, these specialised vehicles were designed for loading and unloading horses at platform level. Four were released covering LMS and BR crimson colour schemes. ☞

Few could have predicted the Crosti '9F' as a ready-to-run model, but what an impressive sight it makes. This is 92027 in original condition carrying BR black without a smoke deflector around its side exhaust.

Drummond's characterful '700' 0-6-0 was a hard working goods engine for the Southern Railway and British Railways Southern Region. New to the range in 2015 this is 30693 – one of four models of this fine design to be released in June.

HORNBY 2015 LOCOMOTIVE RE-RELEASE HIGHLIGHTS

Cat No.	Model	Livery
R3010	SR 'King Arthur' 4-6-0 771 *Sir Sagramore*	SR olive green
R3132	Gresley 'A3' 4-6-2 2599 *Book Law*	LNER lined green
R3143	Class 423 4-VEP Electric Multiple Unit 7830	BR blue and grey
R3181	Class 56 56084	BR 'large logo' blue
R3188	Gresley 'N2' 0-6-2T 69689	BR lined black, late crests
R3215	Eurostar Class 373 Train pack	Eurostar revised livery
R3221	LMS *Duchess of Sutherland* and support coach pack	BR lined green, early crests
R3222	Churchward '42XX' 2-8-0T 4261	GWR green
R3223	Churchward '42XX' 2-8-0T 4257	BR black, late crests
R3224	Churchward '52XX' 2-8-0T 5239	BR black, late crests
R3225	Churchward '72XX' 2-8-2T 7233	GWR green
R3226	Churchward '72XX' 2-8-2T 7218	BR black, early crests
R3227	Thompson 'O1' 2-8-0 63663	BR black, late crests
R3237	Collett 'Castle' 4-6-0 4073 *Caerphilly Castle*	GWR green
R3263	Class 50 50024 *Vanguard*	BR large logo blue
R3264	Class 50 50046 *Ajax*	BR large logo blue
R3265	Class 56 56087	Colas Rail
R3269	Class 43 HST power cars	BR blue and yellow
R3270	Class 43 HST power cars	Midland Mainline
R3271	Class 43 HST power cars	BR InterCity 'executive'
R3284TTS	Gresley 'A1' 4-6-2 4472 Flying Scotsman (TTS)	LNER lined green
R3286TTS	Class 40 D232 *Empress of Canada* (TTS)	BR green
R3287TTS	Class 47 47401 with Twin Track Sound	BR 'large logo' blue
R3289TTS	Class 37 97301 with Twin Track Sound	Network Rail yellow
R3340	Class 402 2-HAL Electric Multiple Unit 2603	BR green, full yellow ends
R3341	Class 402 2-HAL Electric Multiple Unit 2677	BR blue, full yellow ends
R3344	Class 31 31285	Network Rail yellow
R3346	Class 92 92009 *Marco Polo*	DB Schenker red
R3347	Class 92 92019 *Wagner*	EWS triple grey
R3348	Class 67 67016	EWS maroon and gold
R3350	Class 90 90029	DB Schenker red
R3352	Class 153 153329	First Great Western
R3353	Sentinel 4wDH	Balfour Beatty orange
R3354	Sentinel 0-4-0 *Barabel*	Lined maroon
R3355	Sentinel 0-4-0 HO13	Wabtec black
R3365	Class 91 91120	East Coast Trains grey

The GWR 'Hall' 4-6-0 was seen working across the Western network. This new cross RailRoad/main range model debuted in February 2015.

Stanier 57ft non-corridor stock continued Hornby's high reputation for quality carriages.

The passenger stock range expanded with the LMS 57ft non-corridor carriages. These models were unveiled on the Hornby stand at the Warley National Model Railway Exhibition in November 2014 with the range covering the Third, Composite and Brake Third. The real vehicles were built in the 1930s at Derby Works for use on local and commuter services and featured steel panelled sides together with flush glazed windows.

Hornby's high reputation for modelling the famous Pullman carriages continued with announcement and delivery of the all-steel K-Type Pullman cars. Announced in December 2014 the new range of five vehicles arrived in June 2015 offering Kitchen First, Kitchen Third, Parlour First, Parlour Third and Parlour Brake vehicles.

These new vehicles entered service for the Pullman Car Company on the LNER's prestigious 'Queen of Scots' Pullman from 1928, which ran between London King's Cross, Edinburgh and Glasgow. They differed from previous Pullman cars by Hornby in having steel panelling on the outside and large picture windows while inside the vehicles received new interior décor and armchairs.

Diesel sounds

Following the success of the initial batches of Hornby's ground breaking budget Twin Track Sound (TTS) decoder with steam locomotives during 2014, the first of the TTS diesels arrived in January. The RailRoad range Class 37 and Class 40 debuted the potential of the diesel TTS sound decoder and

The 'D16/3' 4-4-0s were a triumph on the real railway and this place in the Hornby range has received a great response. This is 62530 in BR lined black – one of four to be released in 2015.

were joined by the Class 47 in the middle of the year.

The new Hornby DCC TTS decoder, designed in-house, resulted in a remarkably low price for a DCC sound-fitted locomotive. The chassis on each model is fitted with an 8-pin TTS decoder and 28mm diameter speaker.

The decoder features 25 functions which include startup, horns, door slams, fans, primer noises, brake squeal, coupling sounds and much more. In addition, the ability to manually notch the engine revs up or down is impressive using the function keys, offering a more realistic driving experience.

Future prospects

2015 has been a great year for new Hornby releases, but there's plenty more to come with the LNER 'J50' 0-6-0T due in the final weeks of the year in LNER and BR liveries while the highly anticipated LSWR Adams '0415' 4-4-2T is expected to arrive towards the end of January 2016 with three versions covering LSWR and BR liveries due to debut this fine Victorian engine.

The Hornby Development Team is hard at work on its extensive range of projects for 2016 which includes the enticing prospect of a ready-to-run original condition Southern Railway 'Merchant Navy' 4-6-2 and the eagerly awaited Class 71 Bo-Bo electric along with the Peckett 'W4' 0-4-0ST , GWR Collett bow ended standard 57ft corridor stock and Southern Railway Maunsell 58ft non-corridor coaches and even more!

2016 promises to be an even more exciting year and we can't wait to see the results. Ⓗ

HORNBY 2015 NEW TOOLING TIMELINE

Month	Model	Catalogue numbers
Jan	Peppercorn 'K1' 2-6-0	R3242/R3243/R3243A/R3305
Jan	Collett 'Hall' 4-6-0	R3220/R3169/R3170/R3205
Jan	BR 21ton hopper wagon	R6675/R6676/R6677/R6691
Jan	LMS Horsebox	R6678/R6678A/R6679/R6679A
Feb	Worsdell 'J15' 0-6-0	R3230/R3231/R3232
April	LMS 57ft non-corridor Composite	R4656/R4658
April	LMS 57ft non-corridor Third	R4657/R4659
April	LMS 57ft non-corridor Brake Third	R4677/R4677A/R4678/R4678A
June	Drummond '700' 0-6-0	R3238/R3239/R3240/R3304
June	All-Steel K-Type Pullman cars	R4660/R4661/R4662/R4663/R4664
Aug	BR Crosti boilered '9F' 2-10-0	R3273/R3274
Oct	Maunsell 'S15' 4-6-0	R3327/R3328/R3329
Nov	Collett 'King' 4-6-0	R3330/R3331/R3332/R3370TTS

Hornby

YOUR GUIDE TO HORNBY'S FULL PRODUCT RANGE.

PRODUCT LISTING

Train sets 2016

Cat No.	Description
R1125	Somerset Belle (digital train set)
R1126	Mixed Freight (digital train set)
R1138	GWR Passenger Freight
R1140	Caledonian Carrier train set
R1142K	Western Messenger train set
R1151	Caledonian Belle
R1155	Virgin Trains Pendolino
R1156	Eastern Rover train set
R1157	West Coast Highlander train set
R1167	The Flying Scotsman
R1169K	Tornado Pullman Express train set
R1172	The Majestic (digital train set)
R1173	Western Master (digital train set)
R1176	Eurostar
R1177	Gloucester City Pullman
R1179	Santa Express train set
R1180	Postal Express train set
R1183	Master of the Glens
R1184	Western Express (digital train set) with eLink and TTS 'Hall'
R1185	Christmas train set
R1187	Harry Potter Anniversary train set
R1197	Western Master (digital train set) with eLink
R1199	Platinum Digital train set

TrakMat Packs and Accessories

Cat No.	Description
R8217	TrakMat
R8221	Extension Pack A
R8222	Extension Pack B
R8223	Extension Pack C
R8224	Extension Pack D
R8225	Extension Pack E
R8226	Extension Pack F
R8227	TrakMat Accessories, Pack 1
R8228	TrakMat Accessories, Pack 2
R8229	TrakMat Accessories, Pack 3
R8230	TrakMat Accessories, Pack 4
R8231	TrakMat Accessories, Pack 5

Thomas and Friends

Cat No.	Description
R9283	Thomas the Tank Engine
R9284	Percy and the Mail Train
R9285	Thomas Passenger and Goods
R9286	Edward's Day Out
R9287	Thomas
R9288	Percy
R9289	Edward
R9290	James
R9291	Gordon
R9292	Henry
R9293	Annie and Clarabel
R9294	Troublesome Trucks
R9295	James's Composite Coach
R9296	James's Brake Coach
R9297	Gordon's Composite Coach
R9298	Gordon's Brake Coach
R9299	Tanker triple pack
R9300	Wagon triple pack, A
R9301	Wagon triple pack, B
R9302	Old Slow Coach

Steam locomotives 2016

Cat No.	Description
R3404	LMS Fowler 2-6-4T 42334, BR lined black, late crests
R3405	LNER 'J50' 0-6-0T 586, LNER unlined black
R3406	LNER 'J50' 0-6-0T Departmental No. 14, BR black, late crests
R3407	LNER 'J50' 0-6-0T 68959, BR black, early crests
R3408	GWR 'King' 4-6-0 6016 *King Edward V*, GWR shirtbutton green
R3409	GWR 'King' 4-6-0 6002 *King William IV*, BR lined green, late crests
R3410	GWR 'King' 4-6-0 6025 *King Henry III*, BR lined blue, early crests
R3411	SR 'S15' 4-6-0 827, Southern Railway black
R3412	SR 'S15' 4-6-0 30842, BR black, early crests
R3413	SR 'S15' 4-6-0 30831, BR black, late crests
R3414	LNER 'J15' 0-6-0 5444, LNER black
R3415	LNER 'J15' 0-6-0 65477, BR black, early crests
R3416	LNER 'J15' 0-6-0 65464, BR black, late crests
R3417	LNER 'K1' 2-6-0 62065, BR lined black, late crests
R3418	LNER 'K1' 2-6-0 62006, British Railways black
R3419	SR '700' 0-6-0 693, Southern Railway unlined black
R3420	SR '700' 0-6-0 30346, BR black, late crests
R3421	SR '700' 0-6-0 30698, BR black, early crests
R3422	SR '0415' 4-4-2T 3125, SR black with Bulleid lettering
R3423	SR '0415' 4-4-2T 30583, BR lined black, late crests
R3424	LNER 'Q6' 0-8-0 3418, LNER
R3425	LNER 'Q6' 0-8-0 63443, BR black, early crests
R3426	LNER 'Q6' 0-8-0 63429, BR black, late crests
R3427	Peckett 'W4' 0-4-0ST 563, industrial green
R3428	Peckett 'W4' 0-4-0ST 654, dark green and red
R3429	Peckett 'W4' 0-4-0ST 832, dark blue and red
R3430	LNER 'B12' 4-6-0 LNER
R3431	LNER 'B12' 4-6-0 BR lined black, early crests
R3432	LNER 'B12' 4-6-0 BR lined black, late crests
R3433	LNER 'D16/3' 4-4-0 8900, LNER lined apple green
R3434	SR 'Merchant Navy' 4-6-2 (air-smoothed) 21C1 *Channel Packet*, SR malachite green
R3435	SR 'Merchant Navy' 4-6-2 (air-smoothed) 21C3 *Royal Mail*, SR malachite green
R3436	SR 'Merchant Navy' 4-6-2 (air-smoothed) 35028 *Clan Line*, BR lined green
R3437	LNER 'A3' 4-6-2 2503 *Firdaussi*, LNER lined apple green
R3438	LNER 'A4' 4-6-2 4494 *Osprey*, LNER lined apple green
R3439	LNER 'A1' 4-6-2 2554 *Woolwinder*, LNER lined apple green
R3440	LNER 'P2' 2-8-2 2001 *Cock 'O the North*, LNER lined apple green
R3441	LNER 'A4' 4-6-2 4499 *Sir Murrough Wilson*, NE wartime black
R3442	LMS 'Princess Coronation' 4-6-2 6237 *City of Bristol*, LMS lined maroon (streamlined)
R3443	LNER 'A3' 4-6-2 60103 *Flying Scotsman*, BR lined green, late crests
R3444	BR 'Britannia' 4-6-2 70034 *Thomas Hardy*, BR lined green, early crests
R3445	SR 'West Country' 4-6-2 (air-smoothed) 34032 *Camelford*, BR lined green, early crests
R3446	LNER 'O1' 2-8-0 6359, LNER black
R3447	LNER 'B17' 4-6-0 2842 *Kilverston Hall*, LNER lined apple green
R3448	LNER 'B17' 4-6-0 61619 *Welbeck Abbey*, BR lined green, early crests
R3451	LNER 'B1' 4-6-0 61032 *Stembok*, BR lined black, early crests
R3452	GWR 'Grange' 4-6-0 6825 *Llanfair Grange*, BR lined green, late crests
R3453	LMS 'Black Five' 4-6-0 45274, BR lined black, late crests
R3454	GWR 'Castle' 4-6-0 5076 *Drysllwyn Castle*, GWR shirt button lined green
R3455	GWR 'Star' 4-6-0 4013 *Knight of St Patrick*, GWR lined green

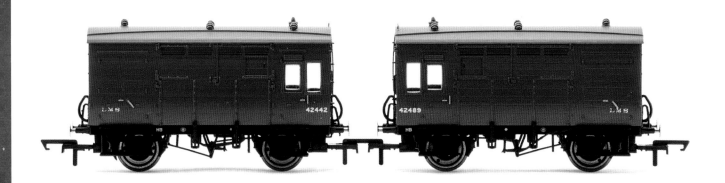

R3456	SR 'King Arthur' 4-6-0 30792 *Sir Hervis de Revel*, BR lined green, early crests
R3457	SR 'T9' 4-4-0 116, Southern Railway olive green
R3458	SR 'Schools' 4-4-0 921 *Shrewsbury*, SR black with Bulleid lettering
R3461	LNER 'L1' 2-6-4T 67702, British Railways lined apple green
R3462	GWR '42XX' 2-8-0T 4287, BR black, late crests
R3463	GWR '5205' 2-8-0T 5231, BR black, early crests
R3464	GWR '72XX' 2-8-2T 7224, BR black, late crests
R3465	LNER 'N2' 0-6-2T 4765, LNER lined black
R3466	Hunslet 'Austerity' 0-6-0ST 22, United Steel Company maroon
R3467	SR 'Terrier' 0-6-0T 751, SECR lined green
R3468	SR 'Battle of Britain' 4-6-2 (rebuilt) 34077 *603 Squadron*, BR lined green, late crests

Twin track sound steam locomotives 2016

Cat No.	Description
R3382TTS	SR 'Merchant Navy' 4-6-2 35023 *Holland Afrika Line,* BR lined green, early crests
R3383TTS	GWR 'Castle' 4-6-0 5050 *Earl of St Germans*, BR lined green, early crests
R3384TTS	GWR 'King' 4-6-0 6006 *King George I*, BR lined green, late crests

R3385TTS	LMS 'Black Five' 4-6-0 45116, BR lined black, early crests
R3386TTS	SR 'Schools' 4-4-0 30933 *King's Canterbury*, BR lined green, late crests
R3387TTS	BR 'Britannia' 4-6-2 70001 *Lord Hurcomb*, BR lined green, early crests
R3395TTS	LNER 'A4' 4-6-2 (RailRoad model) 4468 *Mallard*, LNER garter blue
R3396TTS	BR Crosti '9F' 2-10-0 (RailRoad model) 92025, BR black, early crests
R3459TTS	LMS '2P' 4-4-0 40626, BR lined black, early crests
R3460TTS	LMS '4F' 0-6-0 44918, BR black, late crests

Diesel locomotives 2016

Class	Description
R3341A	2-HAL 2623 BR blue with full yellow ends
R3373	Class 71 E5001, BR green with small yellow panels (NRM)
R3374	Class 71 71012, BR blue
R3376	Class 71 E5022, BR green
R3470	Class 31 D5509, BR green
R3471	Class 50 50026 *Indomitable*, original Network SouthEast
R3472	Class 56 56018, EWS maroon and gold

R3473	Class 56 56108, BR Railfreight grey with red stripe
R3474	Class 90 90015 *The International Brigades*, Virgin Trains
R3475	Class 90 90014 *Norfolk and Norwich Festival*, Greater Anglia
R3476	Class 153 153327, Arriva Train Wales
R3477	Class 153 153321, Regional Railways
R3478	Class 43 43070 *The Corps of Royal Electric and Mechanical Engineers* and 43036, First Great Western
R3479	Class 60 60066, Drax silver
R3480	Class 92 92016 *Brahms*, Railfreight grey with EWS logos
R3481	Class 67 67025 *Western Star*, EWS maroon and gold
R3482	Sentinel 4wDH DH16, Manchester Ship Canal blue
R3483	Sentinel 0-4-0 Crossley and Evans pale blue
R3484	Class 08 13363, BR green, red con rods
R3485	Class 08 08644 *Laira Diesel Depot*, BR blue
R3486	Class 66 66185 *DP World London Gateway*, DB Schenker red
R3487	Class 66 66079, EWS maroon and gold

Twin Track Sound diesel locomotives 2016

Cat No.	Description
R3388TTS	Class 67 67004 *Cairn Gorm*, Caledonian sleeper livery
R3389TTS	Class 60 60012, EW&S maroon and gold
R3390TTS	Class 43 43311 and 43312, Virgin East Coast livery
R3391TTS	Class 31 31239, BR blue
R3392TTS	Class 40 (RailRoad model) 40164, BR blue
R3393TTS	Class 47 (RailRoad model) 47033, Railfreight sub-sector livery
R3394TTS	Class 20 (RailRoad model) 20163, BR blue

RailRoad locomotives 2016

Cat No.	Description
R3356	BR Crosti '9F' 2-10-0 92025, BR black, early crests, weathered
R3490	Class 08 0-6-0 08673, Intercity
R3491	Class 42 B-B D805 *Benbow*, BR green
R3492	Class 20 Bo-Bo 20059, Railfreight grey with red stripe
R3493	Class 87 Bo-Bo 87026 *Sir Richard Arkwright*, BR blue
R3494	LMS 'Black Five' 4-6-0 45025, BR lined black
R3495	LNER 'Hunt' 4-4-0 62760 *The Cotswold*, BR lined black, early crests
R3496	Industrial 0-4-0T Kelly and Son Paper Mill
R3497	Class 55 Co-Co D9016 *Gordon Highlander*, BR two-tone green
R3498	LMS 'Jinty' 0-6-0T 19, Somerset and Dorset Joint Railway blue
R3499	GWR 'Hall' 4-6-0 6946 *Heatherden Hall*, BR lined green, late crests

Train packs locomotives 2016

Cat No.	Description
R3397	LMS Suburban Passenger pack
R3398	Lyme Regis Branch Line pack
R3399	EWS Freight pack
R3400	Last steam hauled Golden Arrow pack
R3401	The Bristolian pack (1935)
R3402	LNER Queen of Scots pack
R3403	Intercity 40th pack
R3501	Virgin East Coast pack

RailRoad train packs 2016

Cat No.	Description
R3488	Diesel freight pack: LMS liveried Class 08, brown van, LMS coal wagon
R3489	GWR freight pack: '101' 0-4-0T, 'Toad' brake van, Broadoak wagon

Carriages 2016

Cat No.	Description
R4131C	LMS 68ft dining car M232M, BR maroon
R4178C	LNER Gresley Corridor composite E10106E, BR carmine and cream
R4179B	LNER Gresley Corridor First E11003E, BR carmine and cream
R4180B	LNER Gresley Corridor Second E12549E, BR carmine and cream
R4181B	LNER Gresley corridor Buffet E9114E, BR carmine and cream
R4234B	LMS Corridor First M1080M, BR maroon
R4235C	LMS Corridor Second M1741M, BR maroon
R4236C	LMS Corridor Brake Second M5806M, BR maroon
R4516B	LNER Gresley Third 21022, LNER varnished teak
R4517B	LNER Gresley Composite 32480, LNER varnished teak
R4518B	LNER Gresley Brake Third 3738, LNER varnished teak
R4534D	BR Maunsell push-pull pack Set 619, BR Southern Region green
R4572A	LNER Thompson Composite 88426, LNER varnished teak
R4573A	LNER Thompson Third 82646, LNER varnished teak
R4574A	LNER Thompson Brake Third 87019, LNER varnished teak
R4656A	LMS 57ft non-corridor Composite 16612, LMS lined maroon
R4657A	LMS 57ft non-corridor Third 11718, LMS lined maroon
R4677B	LMS 57ft non-corridor Brake Third 20754, LMS lined maroon
R4677C	LMS 57ft non-corridor Brake Third 20755, LMS lined maroon
R4679	GWR Collett Corridor Third, 4548, GWR chocolate and cream
R4680	GWR Collett Corridor Brake Third (RH), 5131, GWR chocolate and cream
R4681	GWR Collett Corridor Brake Third (LH), 5132, GWR chocolate and cream
R4682	GWR Collett Corridor Composite (LH), 6520, GWR chocolate and cream
R4683	GWR Collett Corridor Composite (RH), GWR chocolate and cream
R4684	GWR Collett Corridor Third, W4857W, BR carmine and cream
R4685	GWR Collett Corridor Brake Third (RH), W5091W, BR carmine and cream
R4686	GWR Collett Corridor Brake Third (LH), W5092W, BR carmine and cream
R4687	GWR Collett Corridor Composite (LH), W6030W, BR carmine and cream
R4688	GWR Collett Corridor Composite (RH), W6029W, BR carmine and cream
R4689	LMS 57ft non-corridor Composite M16574M, BR maroon
R4690	LMS 57ft non-corridor Third M11912M, BR maroon
R4691	LMS 57ft non-corridor Brake Third M20787M, BR maroon
R4691A	LMS 57ft non-corridor Brake Third M20788M, BR maroon
R4693	All-steel K-Type Pullman Kitchen Third Car No. 67, Pullman umber and cream, grey roof
R4694	All-steel K-Type Pullman Parlour Third Car No. 83, Pullman umber and cream, grey roof
R4695	All-steel K-Type Pullman Brake Third Car No. 80, Pullman umber and cream, grey roof

Cat No.	Description
R4696	All-steel K-Type Pullman Kitchen First *Joan, Pullman* umber and cream, grey roof
R4697	All-steel K-Type Pullman Parlour First *Ursula*, Pullman umber and cream, grey roof
R4698	BR Mk 1 Full Brake E80534, BR carmine and cream
R4699	BR Mk 1 Full Brake S80926, BR Southern Region green
R4700	BR Mk 1 Second Open M4487, BR maroon
R4701	BR Mk 1 Tourist Second Open M3947, BR maroon
R4702	BR Mk 2E Standard Open 5801, Virgin Trains
R4702A	BR Mk 2E Standard Open 5787, Virgin Trains
R4704	BR Mk 2E Brake Standard Open 9507, Virgin Trains
R4705	BR Mk 1 Corridor Second E24162, BR carmine and cream
R4706	BR Mk 1 Corridor Composite E15058, BR carmine and cream
R4707	BR Mk 1 Corridor Brake Second E34010, BR carmine and cream
R4708	BR Mk 1 Corridor Second W24540, BR chocolate and cream
R4709	BR Mk 1 Corridor Composite W15061, BR chocolate and cream
R4710	BR Mk 1 Corridor Brake Second W34290, BR chocolate and cream
R4711	BR MK 1 Corridor Second S24316, BR Southern Region green
R4712	BR Mk 1 Corridor Composite S15913, BR Southern Region green
R4713	BR Mk 1 Corridor Brake Second S34613, BR Southern Region green
R4714	BR Mk 1 Corridor Second M24912, BR maroon
R4715	BR Mk 1 Corridor Composite M15679, BR maroon
R4716	BR Mk 1 Corridor Composite M34672, BR maroon
R4717	SR 58ft eight comp' Brake Third 2639, SR olive green (set 45)
R4718	SR 58ft six comp' Composite 2626, SR olive green
R4719	SR 58ft six comp' Third 6404, SR olive green (set 45)
R4720	SR 58ft nine comp' Third 304, SR olive green
R4729	BR Mk 3 Buffet 40001, BR Intercity blue and grey

Cat No.	Description
R4730	BR Mk 3 First Open 41003, BR Intercity blue and grey
R4730A	BR Mk 3 First Open 41004, BR Intercity blue and grey
R4732	BR Mk 3 Tourist Second Open 42003, BR Intercity blue and grey
R4732A	BR Mk 3 Tourist Second Open 42004, BR Intercity blue and grey
R4734	SR Maunsell Corridor First 7406, Southern Railway malachite
R4735	SR Maunsell Corridor Third 1216, Southern Railway malachite
R4736	SR Maunsell Brake Third 3797, Southern Railway malachite (six compartment)
R4737	SR Maunsell Brake Third 3798, Southern Railway malachite (six compartment)
R4738	Pullman Parlour First *Lydia*, Pullman umber and cream
R4739	Pullman Parlour Third Car No. 34, Pullman umber and cream
R4740	Pullman Kitchen First *Argus*, Pullman umber and cream
R4741	Pullman Kitchen Third Car No. 58, Pullman umber and cream
R4742	Pullman Brake Third Car No. 162, Pullman umber and cream
R4745	SR '2-SET W' coach pack Set 109, BR Southern Region green (BCK, SO)
R4746	SR 58ft eight comp' Brake Second S2637S, BR Southern Region green (set 43)
R4747	SR 58ft six comp' Composite S2629S, BR Southern Region green
R4748	SR 58ft six comp' Second S6402S, BR Southern Region green
R4749	SR 58ft nine comp' Second S267S, BR Southern Region green (set 43)
R4750	BR Mk 3 Trailer Guard Standard 44050, Virgin Trains East Coast
R4751	BR Mk 3 Tourist Second Open 42322, Virgin Trains East Coast
R4751A	BR Mk 3 Tourist Second Open 42130, Virgin Trains East Coast
R4752	BR Mk 3 First Open 41159, Virgin Trains East Coast
R4753	BR Mk 3 Buffet 40708, Virgin Trains East Coast

RailRoad carriages and wagons 2016

Cat No.	Description
R4743	SR composite coach 5505, SR olive green
R4744	SR brake coach 3563, SR olive green
R6784	Open wagons (triple pack), triple pack of private owner hoper wagons

Skaledale buildings 2016

Cat No.	Description
R9801	Modern terrace house
R9802	Modern prefabricated building
R9803	Tin house
R9807	Modern bungalow
R9808	Timber store and workshop
R9811	Shiplap lean-to
R9812	Triple garage
R9813	Ex-barrack rooms
R9815	Covered loading bay
R9816	Wateringbury signalbox
R9817	Raised water tank
R9826	Detached brick garage
R9827	Memorial
R9828	Bakers shop
R9829	Toy shop
R9830	Shoe shop
R9831	Florist
R9832	Restaurant
R9833	Corner pub
R9834	Village tea rooms
R9835	Hardware store
R9836	Granite station building
R9837	Granite station waiting room
R9838	Granite signalbox
R9839	Granite water tower
R9840	Granite engine shed
R9841	Granite goods shed

Skaledale buildings and structures

Cat No.	Description
R8509	Single stone tunnel portal (two)
R8510	Single brick tunnel portal (two)
R8511	Double stone tunnel portal (two)
R8512	Double brick tunnel portal (two)
R8526	Granite wall, pack 1
R8527	Granite wall, pack 2
R8538	Granite wall, pack 3
R8539	Cotswold stone, pack 1
R8540	Cotswold stone, pack 2
R8541	Cotswold stone, pack 3

R8544	Stone tunnel portal side walling	R9512	Concrete platelayers hut	R9774	National Merchant Bank
R8545	Brick tunnel portal side walling	R9639	Great Northern water tower	R9776	Midland signalbox
R8552	Wooden garage	R9643	Thatched cottage (unpainted)	R9777	Weighbridge office
R8574	Gravestones	R9644	Small townhouse (unpainted)	R9778	Butterley station
R8575	Memorial	R9645	Bungalow (unpainted)	R9779	Butterley waiting room
R8576	Garden shed	R9647	Derelict barm	R9780	Locomotive shed
R8577	Dustbins	R9653	Baptist church	R9781	Village hall
R8579	Pillar box	R9662	Modern factory front, low relief	R9782	Utility lamp huts
R8580	Telephone kiosk	R9674	Dent snow huts	R9783	Lamp huts
R8583	Single sided straight platforms (two)	R9709	Headingly insurance office	R9784	Butterley extension building
R8584	Loading bay platform pack	R9715	Lite Bite sandwich bar	R9785	Crossing hut
R8587	Coal stage	R9725	LMS signalbox	R9786	Small signalbox
R8603	Coal staithes	R9726	LMS water tower	R9787	Water tower
R8604	Platform steps pack	R9727	Trackside steps	R9788	Locomotive shed lean to
R8605	Loading stage and crane	R9729	Period signalbox	R9790	Derelict coaches (two)
R8613	Refuse skip (two)	R9732	Rail over river bridge	R9791	Crescent House
R8614	Straight platforms (two)	R9738	NER weighbridge	R9794	Workshop
R8615	Platform ramps (two)	R9740	NER general office	R9796	Village water pump
R8621	Terrace house, left hand	R9741	NER booking office	R9798	Public convenience
R8622	Terrace house, right hand	R9743	NER platform shelter	R9800	Bus shelter
R8626	Fire station	R9744	Brick walls, straight	R9804	Modern detached house
R8641	Footbridge	R9744	NER signalbox	R9805	Garden cottage
R8643	Curved platforms, radius two (two)	R9745	NER small outbuildings	R9806	Railwaymans Arms
R8673	Platform lamps (four)	R9746	NER waiting room	R9809	Garage outbuilding
R8674	Benches (two)	R9753	Model shop	R9810	Corrugated iron workshop
R8675	Modern lineside hut and AWS box set	R9754	Monument	R9814	Platform signalbxox
R8678	Milk churns	R9755	Utility warehouse, low relief	R9818	High Brooms station
R8679	Bicycles (two)	R9756	Highland Mils (low relief)	R9819	High Brooms platform building
R8681	Bus stop, modern	R9757	The chapel, low relief	R9820	Diesel fuel tank
R8682	Greenhouse	R9758	Rainbow Carpets (low relief)	R9821	Wayside halt building
R8696	Police box	R9759	County Hall, low relief	R9822	Steam shed (two road)
R8701	Country police station	R9760	Pickwick Books (low relief)	R9823	Platform subway
R8711	Cement hopper	R9761	Ye Olde Tea Shoppe (low relief)	R9824	Station office
R8745	Brick walls, corners	R9762	Holiday coach access steps	R9825	Railway stores
R8761	Modern telephone kiosk	R9763	Off Your Head barbers shop		
R8762	Litter bin (three)	R9764	Canons Newsagents		
R8763	Letter box (two)	R9765	Warren & Co Estate Agents		

People and animals

Cat No.	Description
R560	City people (seven)
R561	People sitting (six)
R562	Town people (eight)
R563	Working people (six)
R564	Farm people (six)
R565	Farm animals
R767	Sheep (10)
R768	Cows (10)

R8787	Pillbox
R8788	Corrugated nissen hut
R8797	Newspaper kiosk
R8977	Brick walling, straight (four)
R8978	Brick walling, corners (four)
R8979	Brick walling, gates and piers (one gate, two brick sections)
R8986	Brick garage
R8987	Anderson shelter

R9766	Maestro Market
R9767	Andrew James butchers
R9768	The pharmacy
R9769	The Pine Shop
R9770	The corner shop
R9771	Three Barrels wine bar
R9772	High Street Dental
R9773	Kings Arms

Digital Accessories

Cat No.	Description
R8144	RailMaster
R8213	Select digital controller
R8214	Elite digital controller
R8232	Digital electric point clips (20 per pack)
R8235	Select walkabout digital controller
R8236	RJ12 4-wire 3M lead
R8237	RJ12 connecting socket
R8238	Reverse loop module
R8239	Power and signal booster
R8241	Digital power track
R8242	Digital power connecting clip
R8245	Sapphire decoder (8-pin/21-pin)
R8247	Accessory decoder
R8249	Locomotive decoder (8-pin)
R8266	RJ12 connecting leads
R8312	eLink and RailMaster

Track and accessories

Cat No.	Description
P9000	Standard wall plug transformer
R044	Lever switch, 'passing contact'
R046	Lever switch, 'on-on'
R047	Lever switch, 'on-off'
R070	Electrically operated turntable
R169	Home signal for junction (red arms)
R170	Distant signal for junction (yellow arms)
R171	Single home signal (red arm)
R172	Single distant signal (yellow arm)
R207	Track fixing pins
R406	Colour light signal
R600	Straight (168mm)
R601	Double straight (335mm)

Cat No.	Description
R602	Power connecting clip (analogue)
R603	Long straight (670mm)
R604	First radius curve
R605	First radius double curve
R606	Second radius curve
R607	Second radius double curve
R608	Third radius curve
R609	Third radius double curve
R610	Short straight (38mm)
R614	Left-hand diamond crossing (168mm)
R615	Right-hand diamond crossing (168mm)
R618	Isolating track (168mm)
R620	Railer/uncoupler (168mm)
R621	Flexible track (970mm)
R626	Underlay sheets
R628	Curve (for use with R8076 'Y' point)
R638	Underlay strip
R643	Half curve
R910	Rail joiners
R920	Isolated rail joiners
R8012	HM2000 power controller
R8014	Point motor
R8015	Point motor housing for R8014
R8072	Left-hand standard point (168mm)
R8073	Right-hand standard point (168mm)
R8074	Left-hand curved point
R8075	Right-hand curved point
R8076	'Y' point
R8077	Left-hand express point (245mm)
R8078	Right-hand express point (245mm)
R8087	Track rubber
R8090	Semi-flexible track (914mm)
R8145	Track-Master layout planning software
R8201	Link wire

Cat No.	Description
R8206	Power track (168mm)
R8211	Rolling road
R8212	Rolling road spare rollers
R8241	Digital power track (168mm)
R8243	Surface mounted point motor
R8244	Uncoupling unit
R8250	Standard train controller
R8261	Fourth radius curve
R8262	Fourth radius double curve

Plastic buildings and accessories

Cat No.	Description
R076	Footbridge
R083	Bufferstop
R180	Viaduct (332mm)
R189	Brick bridge (111mm)
R334	Station over-roof
R394	Hydraulic bufferstop
R460	Straight platform (168mm)
R462	Large radius curved platform (outside second radius curve)
R463	Small radius curved platform (inside first radius curve)
R464	Platform end ramp (127mm)
R495	Subway platform (168mm)
R499	River bridge (334mm)
R510	Platform shelter
R513	Platform fencing
R514	Platform canopies
R530	Pylons
R537	Trackside fencing
R574	Trackside accessories
R590	Station halt

R617	Uncoupling ramp
R636	Level crossing, double track
R645	Level crossing, single track
R657	Girder bridge (168mm)
R658	Inclined piers
R659	High level piers
R660	Elevated track sidewalls
R909	Elevated track support set
R8000	Country station
R8001	Waiting room
R8002	Goods shed
R8003	Water tower
R8004	Engine shed
R8005	Signalbox
R8006	Diesel maintenance depot
R8007	Booking hall
R8008	Grand suspension bridge (1,372mm)
R8009	Station terminus

Rolling stock accessories

Cat No.	Description
R573	Locomotive super detail pack
R8096	Disc wheels
R8097	Disc wheels with holes
R8098	Spoked wheels
R8099	Coupling assembly (10 pack)
R8218	14.1mm disc coach wheels
R8219	NEM close couplings
R8220	NEM Hornby couplings
R8234	14.1mm four-hole wheels
R8264	14.1mm two-hole coach wheels
R8267	Medium width couplings
R8268	Large width couplings

Skale Scenics

Cat No.	Description
R8802	Light tan gravel, fine
R8806	Tan gravel, medium
R8823	Beige mixed gravel, fine
R8827	White gravel, medium
R8828	White gravel, coarse
R8831	Dark brown rocks
R8836	Medium green foliage-fibre clusters, medium
R8837	Medium green foliage-fibre clusters, coarse
R8839	Dark green foliage-fibre clusters, medium
R8842	Early autumn foliage-fibre clusters, medium
R8843	Early autumn foliage-fibre clusters, coarse
R8844	Late autumn foliage-fibre clusters, fine
R8845	Late autumn foliage-fibre clusters, medium
R8846	Late autumn foliage-fibre clusters, coarse
R8862	Golden brown field grass
R8863	Light green field grass
R8864	Dark green field grass
R8866	Green blended turf, medium
R8868	Autumn blended turf, medium
R8870	Early autumn blended turf, medium
R8871	Late autumn blended turf, fine
R8872	Late autumn blended turf, medium
R8873	Soil turf, fine
R8874	Earth turf, fine
R8875	Earth turf, coarse
R8876	Golden straw turf, fine
R8877	Golden straw turf, coarse
R8878	Yellow straw turf, fine
R8879	Yellow straw turf, coarse
R8881	Burnt grass turf, coarse

R8882	Moss green turf, fine
R8883	Moss green turf, coarse
R8885	Dark green turf, coarse
R8886	Conifer green turf, fine
R8887	Conifer green turf, medium
R8888	Conifer green turf, coarse
R8889	Forest green turf, fine
R8890	Forest green turf, medium
R8891	Forest green turf, coarse
R8896	Spring green turf, fine
R8897	Spring green turf, coarse
R8899	Martian green turf, medium
R8901	Chile Pine (63mm)
R8903	Poplar (100mm)
R8904	Cedar (100mm)
R8913	Deciduous (75mm)
R8915	Sycamore (75mm)
R8919	Birch (100mm)
R8921	Ash tree (75mm)
R8926	Scots Pine (75mm)
R8927	Scots Pine (100mm)
R8944	Sycamore tree kit (75mm-100mm)
R8954	Beige gravel, coarse

Skale Lighting

Cat No.	Description
R8947	Power strip
R8948	Plugs (six)
R8949	Sockets (two)
R8950	Fuses (four)
R8951	Extension wire
R8952	Bulbs (four)

GUARD   M 20769 M

Glossary

There are hundreds of terms used in model railway language.
This is a guide to the basics to get you started…

A

AC	Alternating Current. Electric current which reverses direction at rapid regular intervals.
Accessory decoder	Fixed location digital decoder that controls signals, point motors and other accessories.
Address	Identifying number for DCC fitted locomotive or accessory decoder.
A1A-A1A	Diesel locomotive wheel arrangement. Two six-wheeled driving bogies, centre axle unpowered.
Airbrush	Air powered paint spraying device.
Amp	Unit of measurement for electric current.
Analogue control	Conventional train control using voltage regulation and reverse polarity.

B

Back to back	Measured distance between the inside edges of two wheels on an axle.
Backscene	Printed or painted rear fascia on a layout.
Ballast	Crushed stone chippings used to form trackbed. Aids drainage and stability on the real railway.
Baseboard	Flat base for building a layout, usually assembled from wood.
BCK	Corridor Brake Composite.
BG	Gangway Brake.
B-B	Diesel-hydraulic wheel arrangement. Two four wheeled bogies, axles each driven by cardan shafts.
Bo-Bo	Electric and diesel-electric locomotive wheel arrangement. Two four-wheeled driving bogies each axle driven by individual traction motor.
Bogie	Wheel unit on locomotives and rolling stock.
Boiler	Cylindrical vessel filled with heat tubes used to create steam.
Bolster wagon	Flat open wagon featuring horizontal bolsters to keep load proud of wagon floor.
Box van	Closed wagon for transport of goods.
Brake van	Vehicle fitted with brakes which can be applied from within, usually located at the end of a train.
BR	British Railways, formed in 1948.
Branch	Railway line which diverges from the main line.
Brick paper	Modelling paper printed with scaled brickwork.
BSK	Corridor Brake Second.
Buckeye	Type of inter-vehicle coupling unit, designed for simple automatic coupling and uncoupling.
Bullhead rail	Identical rail profile for upper and lower section of rail.
Bufferbeam	Metal beam which supports buffers, couplings and pipework at each end of locomotives and rolling stock.
Buffers	Metal extensions found at each end of a railway vehicle, designed to absorb impacts.
Bufferstop	Device to prevent rail vehicles passing the end of a section of rail.

C

Cab control	Analogue layout wiring of sections allowing it to be switched between controllers.
Cameo	Small highly detailed modelling scene.
Cantrail	Area above the doors on each side of a railway vehicle to which the roof is attached.
Cassette	Type of fiddle yard device. Movable storage unit designed to hold a specific length of train off scene.
Catch point	Railway safety device featuring a single trailing point blade. Designed to protect the main line from runaway vehicles.
Catenary	Overhead wires that supply power to electric trains.
C-C	Diesel-hydraulic wheel arrangement. Two bogies, each with three axles driven by cardan shafts
CCT	Covered Carriage Truck.
CDU	Capacitor Discharge Unit. Provides short pulses of high output power for solenoid point motors.
Check rail	Short piece of rail in points/turnouts to guide wheels accurately through the frog.
CK	Corridor Composite.
Co-Co	Diesel locomotive wheel arrangement. Two six-wheeled driving bogies with each axle driven by its own traction motor.
Colour light signal	Electrically powered signal fitted with coloured bulbs or LEDs, usually combinations of red, yellow and green.
Command station	Control hub of a DCC operated layout.
Consisting	Two or more locomotives operating together using the same DCC address.
Continuous loop	Most common type of railway layout, which operates in a full circle or oval.
Contact adhesive	Glue specifically designed to create strong solid bonds and capable of sticking to itself.
Controller	Provides regulated power control for a model railway layout.
Cork sheet	Suitable for track laying use as it absorbs noise. Available in a choice of thicknesses.
Couplings	Means of linking one railway vehicle to another.
Craft knife	Precision cutting knife suitable for modelling.
Crossover	A pair of turnouts/points on parallel lines allowing trains to cross from one track to another.
CR	Caledonian Railway.
Cutting	Trench-like shape with sloping walls and railway line running along the base.
CV	Configuration Variable. Programmable DCC decoder settings.

D

DC	Direct Current. Electric current which flows at a constant state.
DCC	Digital Command Control. Model railway digital control system.
DCC Booster	Provides extra power rating to the track to improve DCC signals.
DCC fitted	Model supplied with factory fitted DCC decoder.
DCC ready	Model supplied with DCC decoder socket only.
DCC sound fitted	Model supplied with factory or supplier fitted DCC sound decoder and speaker.
Decoder	Printed circuit board for operating model railway locomotives and accessories.
DEMU	Diesel Electric Multiple Unit.
Diorama	Highly detailed model scene, non working.
Distant signal	Railway signal which cannot display a danger aspect. Displays a caution that next signal may be at danger.
DMU	Diesel Multiple Unit.
Double slip	Narrow diamond crossing featuring four sets of point blades and allowing great flexibility in operation.
DPU	Diesel Parcels Unit.
DPDT	Double pole double throw electrical circuit switch.
Dry brushing	Technique using an almost dry paintbrush to enhance detail or weather a model.

E

Embankment	Raised area of earth for maintaining or changing height of a railway line where terrain fluctuates.
Embossed styrene	Sheets of polystyrene (plastic) embossed with scale stone, brick or corrugated etchings.
EMU	Electric Multiple Unit.
End to end	Type of model railway layout which operates from one end to another and back again.
Engine Shed	Building used to maintain and sometimes store locomotives. Also known as Motive Power Depot.

F

Feather	Series of route indicator lights attached to colour light signals at junctions.
Fiddle yard	Storage area on a layout.
Firebox	Used as a heat source to create heat in the tubes of the boiler. Fired by coal or oil depending on the locomotive design.
Fishplates	See rail joiners.
Fitted goods	Freight train comprising wagons which are all fitted with air or vacuum brakes controlled by the driver.
FK	Corridor First.
Flanges	Lip on locomotive and rolling stock wheel sets to prevent them from derailing.
Flexible track	Lengths of track which can be gently bent to create curved or straight formations.
Flywheel	Additional metal weight on motor drive shaft to improve motor performance
FO	Open First.
Frog	Crossing point of two rails on a set of points/turnout, also known as the 'vee' or 'crossing'.
Function output	Used to control functions on Digital Command Control locomotives or coaches such as lights or sound files.

G

Gantry signal	Elevated metal bridge featuring several signals spanning multiple tracks.
Gauge	Distance between the running rails on a length of track.
GCR	Great Central Railway.
GER	Great Eastern Railway.
GNR	Great Northern Railway.
Ground frame	Series of levers for controlling turnouts/points, usually in station yards or remote locations.
Guard iron	Metal bar ahead of leading or trailing wheels
GUV	General Utility Van.
GWR	Great Western Railway.